Turned-Bowl Design

Turned-Bowl Design

Richard Raffan

UNWIN HYMAN

London

Cover photo: Voamboana; 6¾-in. (175mm) diameter. Photo by Concept Photo, Hobart, Tasmania, Australia.

First printing: October 1987

First published in Great Britain by Unwin Hyman, an imprint of Unwin Hyman Limited, 1988.

Unwin Hyman Limited
Denmark House, 37-39 Queen Elizabeth Street, London SE1 2QB
and 40 Museum Street, London WC1A 1LU

Raffan, Richard.
Turned-bowl design.

1. Bowls (Tableware)—Design and construction   2. Woodwork
I. Title

745.593 NK9604

ISBN 0-04-440132-9

Typeset by The Taunton Press, Inc., Newtown, Connecticut 06470, USA.
Printed and bound by W.A. Krueger Company, New Berlin, Wisconsin 53151, USA.

A FINE WOODWORKING Book

FINE WOODWORKING® is a trademark of The Taunton Press, Inc., registered in the U.S. Patent and Trademark Office.

Contents

Introduction

CHECKING my dictionaries recently, I found that a bowl is generally defined as a nearly hemispherical vessel used to contain liquids or foods, whose width is greater than its height. This book contains my thoughts on designing and making such bowls. I have included very little information about cutting techniques, since these are explained in detail in *Turning Wood with Richard Raffan* (The Taunton Press, Newtown, Conn., 1985).

Of all the objects that can be turned on a lathe, the bowl has attracted the most interest among amateurs and professional woodturners. Indeed, professional reputations are often built on bowls, even though the bulk of an income may be derived from some form of centerwork or lower order of facework. Why? I think a good bowl is almost always more spectacular than a turned box, kitchen scoop or breadboard, no matter how unusual the grain or how well made these may be. The larger, fuller form of a bowl better exhibits all aspects of grain and color. The amateur might be attracted by the ease with which he can make a stunning and functional bowl, the professional by the speed with which he can repay his debts.

It is easy to produce a bowl that, by virtue of its rich color and/or wild grain patterns, will draw gasps of admiration. Along these lines, the early 1980s saw the proliferation of the waney-edged bowl and its bastard cousin, the "bowl form." These featured every split, hole and defect imaginable, located without apparent heed to the most elementary aesthetic or practical considerations. Over the years, I have also heard many woodworkers talk of revealing that which is hidden in the timber. This is all very humble, but it too often reflects a willingness to rely on quality of wood to carry a poorly designed or badly executed piece of work. Other turners claim an interest in form and lavish great attention on the profile, but pay scant notice to the inside.

What is not so easy to accomplish is the creation of a bowl that fully satisfies both hand and eye. Because all wood fades and mellows with age, I focus my attention on form and tactile qualities. Eventually, they will be all that's left, and if these aspects are found wanting no one will bother to keep the bowl. Allowing for the fact that there is always room for refinement and that most bowls are made primarily for money, I would like to think that creative woodturners will nonetheless aspire to the nebulous ideals of perfection. If you reach beyond the gloss of attractive grain and a polished profile, there's a good chance that your bowls will not only feel good and function well, but grace the eye when not in use.

This book describes my personal approach to making bowls and is the sum total of my experience to date. As a bowl maker of nearly 17 years, I have tried many different forms, a selection of which are shown here along with examples made by some of my students and colleagues. Every bowl is manifestly of wood—I have not ventured into the currently popular techniques of obliterating the wood with paint or plastics. You will find examples of good bowls and really bad bowls, as well as others that I think just miss the mark. The mistakes are sometimes more valuable than the successes, as they provide typical examples of what we all should strive to avoid.

Style and originality Your personal style will develop unless rigorously contained. Even in a world where everything seems to have been done before, it's easy to stand out from the crowd. To create an object that is easily identifiable as yours, you have no need to resort to the contrived "creativity" so highly regarded in art circles. Your own sense of balance and proportion, along with your quirky little ways of doing things, will come through in your work.

Whether the result is judged by the world as something to which others should aspire is another matter. I know that if I had ten competent turners copy one bowl, the results would look identical from across a room. They will still look similar at close range, but distinctions in surface quality or edge treatments will be easy to see. Pick the bowls up and you will begin to notice great differences in weight and balance.

This is due, at least in part, to the different ways each of us interprets measurements and tolerances. We do not work with the precision of engineers—the medium won't allow it. If I need an exact measurement, for example, I cut a fraction oversize and work down to the final dimension. Other turners have a different approach, or perhaps do the same thing, but slightly differently.

We should take a good look at what has been done by previous generations and emerge from those traditions, like traditional potters or basket weavers, by refinishing and fine-tuning many forms through trial and error. It is our good fortune that great quantities of source material from all over the world exist in museums, books and magazines. Stimuli abound. We need only pick out what we like and, building on that inspiration and lots of boring, repetitive practice, develop our own style and traditions. Forget about catering to a market or impressing your critics. Create for yourself and, as your freed spirit emerges, your bowls are bound to benefit.

Pricing As your house fills with bowls and you feel embarrassed about giving away yet another to some aunt who already has 50, you might consider selling a few. This raises the eternally vexing question: How much should I charge?

Unless you desperately need the money, don't under-price. I offer this partly as a plea on behalf of professionals everywhere, who have suffered greatly from amateurs interested only in "covering costs." If you want to cover the cost of your timber, why not do it by selling one bowl, rather than selling ten bowls at one tenth the price? It is easy to find bowls at local craft markets selling for less than the cost of the timber from which they were made. This is a general disservice. It creates the impression that all other similar bowls are expensive, and it leads a customer to expect such a bargain in the future, which may backfire on the bowl's maker.

So what is a reasonable price? Most professionals charge for the time it takes to make the bowl, plus the value of the wood, plus an amount for fixed costs, plus whatever they can get away with. Amateurs, or even budding professionals, cannot arrive at a reasonable price this way, so, for a start, you need to know how long it would take you to make a given bowl if you were experienced, and base your costing on that estimate.

I have a rule of thumb for calculating how long I will take to make a bowl, which corresponds with the time any skilled tradesman might expect to take. My formula works well on all sizes in excess of 6 in. (150mm) in diameter—I simply multiply the diameter by the height to arrive at the approximate time in minutes. For example: 6 in. x 3 in. = 18 minutes. (The metric calculation is similar, but the answer is divided by six: 15cm x 7.5cm = 112.5 ÷ 6 = 18.75 minutes.) There is enough room built into this equation to cover the occasional off-day when I have a head cold. In practice, the manufacturing usually takes less time, but the price is based on the assumption that, if replacement orders come along, I might take longer next time.

Once you've established the time it takes to make a bowl you must decide how much to charge per hour. I base this on the average earnings or a standard wage, announced regularly in the media, for, say, miners or teachers. Add to this a fixed hourly cost for power, heating, insurance and all other operating expenses. In my case, this works out to an additional 5%. Finally, add the current market value of your wood. The fact that you may have come by it for nothing is irrelevant—you must consider what it will cost to replace.

Now you have the base price for your bowl. This is the price at which your most aggressive competitors will sell. But most people add a bit for the dramatic grain or their reputation. Some turners, and I admit to being one of them, are able to charge quite a lot more on all manner of questionable grounds such as notoriety, quality of work and so on. How much extra you decide to charge for your expertise in technique or design, or just advertising ability, is between you and your ego.

Richard Raffan
Canberra, Australia
October 1987

Finding Wood

N this earth, there are more than a thousand species of trees and many sizeable woody shrubs you might turn. Timbers are classified broadly as hardwoods, which are deciduous, and softwoods, which are coniferous. There are soft hardwoods, such as balsa, and hard softwoods, such as southern yellow pine in the United States and some English yew. But, in general, softwoods grow faster, resulting in a more open grain than that of the slower-growing hardwoods. The open end grain of the softwoods is more difficult to cut cleanly, so I prefer to turn hardwoods. In areas where hardwoods are not readily available, such as Scandinavia or New Zealand, there is a long tradition of turning local pines and firs.

Plenty of books have been written about timber, its properties and uses, and you should refer to these for information regarding specific woods. (I recommend particularly *Understanding Wood* by R. Bruce Hoadley [Newtown, Conn.: The Taunton Press, Inc., 1980].) Keep in mind, as you read, that there are exceptions to every rule. Some of my best and worst experiences at the lathe have been with what appeared to be almost identical samples of the same species. Tasmanian huon pine, for example, is widely regarded as a forgiving material, easy to cut and to finish. But I have encountered samples with twisted and pithy grain that defied every attempt to achieve a smooth surface. Similar-looking pieces of the same wood were so hard that I needed to regrind the tool after every few cuts. Fortunately, it is often possible to detect the likeli-

The turner's standard woodpile includes short sections of green logs and stacks of sawn boards.

hood of such problems in advance, and in later chapters I will describe what to look for.

This chapter deals with the business of locating your raw material. Whenever I go off on a wood hunt, be it for logs or boards, I am looking for the same things. First, especially since I earn my living selling bowls, I want wood that is easy to work, and that won't present me with too many unanticipated problems. I do not believe in working woods that are notoriously difficult or ridiculously expensive—no matter how dramatic the grain. Life is too short to expend valuable time on recalcitrant raw material. I look for wood that is known to work well, but perhaps with a fiddleback ripple or burl, or strong color, which will enable me to cater to market demands. If the wood is devoid of a strong grain pattern—which I prefer—then it must be able to take the detail of beads or coves well, such as African blackwood, holly or one of the fruitwoods. If it has subtle color variations, so much the better.

Sources One of the major advantages of woodturning in general, and bowl turning in particular, is that you are able to utilize small or irregular pieces of wood that the rest of the timber trades would never even consider. The good news is that what others have rejected often is precisely what the turner is looking for. The bad news is that the folks who sell wood have woken up to this fact, and prices have risen accordingly. Yesterday's scrap pile is today's "turning stock."

You can purchase timber from sawmills and timber merchants, or lumberyards and do-it-yourself outlets. There is also a great deal of wood virtually lying around in towns and cities or any place where there are buildings, and it is often available for the asking.

Sawmills Since sawmills are, metaphorically, nearest the standing tree, they should therefore give you the best deal of all the commercial wood outlets. If you plan to sell bowls for a living, they will be your most likely source of material. Sawmills fall into two main groups: Some saw only what is harvested locally and others handle imported logs. Increasingly, those in the latter group are becoming merchants more than sawyers, because the current trend is to mill the trees near where they are harvested. (In the case of imported timber, this means the country of origin.)

Any sawmill should be able to cut a log to your requirements, although many large operations are not anxious to accommodate a small order. The mills most likely to help you are the small ones, where often you can watch the operation and even be of some assistance. No matter where I've lived—in small towns or on the outskirts of larger cities, in England and Australia—I have always managed to find a small sawmill to break down logs to my specifications. They usually prefer to do this at the end of their workday so that the mill's normal production flow of building or fencing material is not affected.

Forest trees should present few problems for the sawyer, but those coming from more "civilized" areas should be checked for metal. Farmers are notorious for stapling barbed wire around trees, and the trees I climbed as a boy had innumerable 6-in. (150mm) nails hammered in as a climbing aid. The bark and timber have long since enveloped these to provide a nightmare for some sawyer. You may be able to spot some uneven grain where wood has grown around metal, but in London (and I'm sure in many other cities), trees can have shrapnel buried deep within. And since pigeons like to sit in English elms, these tend to be peppered with lead shot.

Considering this risk, your sawyer might be unwilling to cut a suspicious log unless you guarantee to pay for any blade damage. Don't for a moment think him unreasonable: Despite the common use of metal detectors, foreign objects still sneak into the system. They may even survive to present you with a chipped gouge at the lathe. I once found a staple and a 4-in. (100mm) dia. iron ring deep within a bowl. On another occasion I watched an old bottle, which had been lodged in a tree crotch, demolish a good many teeth on a very large bandsaw. If, however, you are buying one of the mill's own logs, which is then sawn to your requirements, the mill should bear the responsibility.

There are real risks associated with sawmilling in general, and with sawing scavenged wood in particular, but if you can find yourself an accommodating sawyer, it is wonderful. As the log rolls onto the carriage, you must decide what you want based on what it appears to offer. With each slice of the saw blade, new opportunities present themselves and critical decisions must be made on the spot: Should the log be rolled, or not? How wide do I make the next cut? The experience can be both intimidating and exhilarating.

If a sawyer is prepared to put himself out to meet your eccentric requirements, be sure to reciprocate with a bowl or two when you pay the bill. Remember that most mills cater to industry and may not understand your needs so readily. A gift bowl will not only foster a bit of goodwill, but may keep you in the sawyer's mind in the future when an unusual log gets dumped in his yard. I find that this practice pays off, especially when making initial contacts. Many mills also keep a small collection of treen to show potential customers what can be done with the raw material.

Before you leave the mill yard, don't forget to take a look at the scrap pile. Even the largest bandsaws can handle only certain lengths, and if the tree-fellers have cut the logs too long they will need to be shortened. The often sizeable off-cuts that result are usually deposited in a corner of the yard before being carted off to the local dump or to the sawyer's fireplace.

Timber merchants   Often these establishments will not have even a handsaw on the premises. Their business is the selling of sawn boards in large volume to the building and furniture trades. They generally prefer to load you up using a forklift truck. So if you are driving a station wagon or small pick-up truck, it is wise to carry a saw so that you can cut any really long boards to fit.

Before the advent of the small, inexpensive electric chainsaw, I carried a portable circular saw for this purpose. Since this meant that any board in excess of 3 in. (75mm) thick had to be cut from both sides, I also carried a square, which I used to transfer my line around the board. Chainsaws are a lot easier. These days, I carry an electric chainsaw and my own extension cord, which I find to be by far the most convenient arrangement. (See Chapter 2 for more on converting timber.)

The large timber merchants often have an assortment of odds-and-ends—perhaps a few boards left over from a large order, or a pile of big off-cuts—that would easily fill your vehicle. You will likely find more than enough to satisfy the requirements of any small production shop. When I started out, this was the stuff I went after. I usually got it cheaply, having done the merchant a favor by helping to clear his yard.

Such a source may be ideal if you are in the business of very limited production runs of "one-off" pieces, as I am. I get to try different woods, which is a lot of fun and also satisfies the retail craft shops that buy my work. It gives them more variety in their stock—always an advantage when it comes to sales.

When you deal with timber merchants, there is always the satisfaction of getting a bargain. But be wary. Sometimes you can lose out quite badly. Consider carefully what you might get out of each chunk of wood. The larger, more expensive pieces may prove to be cheaper in the long run, leaving you with less waste and requiring less time and effort to convert into bowl blanks.

Of late, many timber merchants have become aware of the proliferation of amateur and professional turners, and have made efforts to cater to their needs. Some merchants take the time to separate their off-cuts, odd boards or turning squares, which makes them easy to find and to pick through. They often carry a good stock and variety of rare hardwoods, both in logs and smaller billets. Some even wax their bowl blanks to reduce splitting, which is a very handy service—although the most expensive way to buy wood.

Such timber dealers advertise regularly in the woodworking and hobby magazines, or you may find one by making inquiries at your local sawmill or lumberyard or in the Yellow Pages. If you're lucky, you may be within a few hours' drive of one of these establishments. If not, most of them have a good delivery service that will enable you to order by mail or telephone.

If at all possible, however, I suggest you take a good look at what you are buying before you pay. It could save you a great deal of wasted time later on and prevent your having to write off an unsuitable load. Besides, if you can cull through the wood pile yourself, there is always the chance of finding something exceptional.

Lumberyards and do-it-yourself stores   These places cater more to carpenters and joiners than to woodturners, and I would consider myself lucky to find good bowl material there. If a lumberyard has any thick boards at all, it is unlikely that you'll find any wider than 4 in. (100mm) or 6 in. (150mm). If you are interested in laminating bowl blanks, however, then this could be your best source of material. It will almost certainly have been kiln-dried, and should be relatively stable and ready to go.

Scavenging   The theory is lovely: There is all that wood being chopped in your neighborhood, so why not make use of it? Local road and park crews regularly prune or fell trees to clear streets and power lines. People fell trees in their backyard to let in more light, or to allow a better view of the neighbors. Quite often they are glad to let you pick up the wood, saving them the effort and a trip or two to the dump.

As usual, the reality is slightly different—you have to act quickly because nobody wants the mess around for longer than is necessary. But if you are alert and have a predatory eye, it is amazing what you might discover. If you see a tree being felled or relieved of a few big branches, speak to the people doing the job and they'll most likely be happy to accommodate you. It might also pay to keep in touch with your local tree surgeon. A wide variety of trees are grown in most cities, and you might land something really special that you otherwise would miss.

Using enterprise and muscle, the turner can uncover a vast range of roadside timber in many parts of the world.

Some years ago, I harvested a truly wonderful laburnum stump, which was blocking a neighbor's driveway and breaking up the street pavement. (A couple of bowls repaid the favor.) The wood worked beautifully and yielded several dozen little bowls. Since then I have kept an eye open for similar logs, but have rarely been in the right place at the right time.

Demolition sites can yield a lot of useful material, and you know it will be well seasoned, too. (There are different considerations in turning dry and wet wood, and these are discussed in detail in Chapters 3 and 6.) In New Zealand, many turners earn a good living turning kauri-pine beams reclaimed from old buildings. In England, I have used centuries-old oak, salvaged from restored churches and demolished farm buildings. If you see an old community hall or warehouse being knocked down, it could be worth a closer look. Many old buildings were made of fine materials, and it would be a waste if the beams ended up in a fireplace or buried under tons of garbage.

Over the years, I have sold many bowl blanks that were gathering dust in the corners of my workshop and shed. Every one was perfectly usable, but the size or grain or figure never seemed to be quite right for me. Most of them went to amateur turners, or those starting out in business. You might approach a local professional just in case they, too, feel like shedding a bit of stock which they probably will never use. It's a good way to get going, but soon enough you'll want to cut your own blanks.

Woodturners are blessed with the ability to use timber from many different sources, including material that other tradesmen typically overlook.

FINDING
WOOD
13

Converting Timber

IN a perfect world logs would remain stable as they season. They might shrink a bit, but never split. A very few timbers, like teak or mahogany, almost achieve this ideal, but most of the woods you'll encounter will warp, twist and check before they reach equilibrium.

Before you begin to convert a log or board into bowl stock, you'll find it helpful to understand how wood reacts during seasoning. If you know anyone who can guide you in the beginning, you might avoid some major blunders, although you should be prepared for these sooner or later. Indeed, there is no substitute for first-hand experience—you are unlikely to forget the lesson gained from buying a poor parcel of timber, and I doubt you'll make the same mistake twice.

The stability of a board is related to the alignment of the grain within it, as shown in the drawing on the facing page. The board that's least likely to move during seasoning will be quartersawn *(A)*: The growth rings lie at roughly 90° to the wide faces of the board. A quartersawn board will remain relatively square while it shrinks across its width. In a flatsawn board *(B)*, the growth rings lie closer to parallel to the board faces and the board will cup away from the heart as it dries. If the heart, or pith, of the log is off-center in a flatsawn board *(C)*, the board will warp unevenly, with the tightest part of the warped curve near the central growth rings.

As soon as a tree is felled it begins to dry out. Newly felled logs are very wet and will shrink dramatically in diameter as they dry, although hardly at all in length. Moisture leaves a log most rapidly

This black-heart sassafras was felled in the thick forest of northwest Tasmania. The forest floor, with its mass of debris and opportunistic plants, made the removal of long lengths of timber impossible. It was still laborious, even in these small sections, with each lump weighing about 85 lb. (40kg).

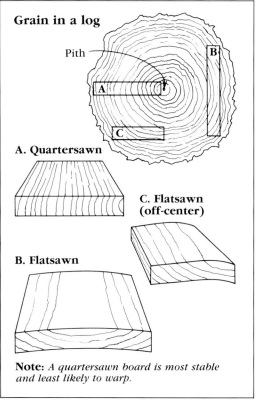

Grain in a log

Pith

A

B

C

A. Quartersawn

B. Flatsawn

C. Flatsawn (off-center)

Note: *A quartersawn board is most stable and least likely to warp.*

through its cut ends, and these are likely to split. So if you can convert a log before it starts to degrade, you'll get the most out of it.

In any case, always anticipate the worst: maximum shrinkage, twisting, warping and splitting; that all stressed wood will crack; that all knots will fall out. If this doesn't occur, count it as a bonus. Here are a few examples of what to look for when you meet a piece of timber for the first time.

Splits and cracks End-grain checks are responsible for a lot of waste. Usually they are obvious, although you will come across some really sneaky ones that only show themselves when the surface is cut very cleanly or, in extreme cases, after the wood has been sanded and polished.

I try to avoid splits and cracks (known also as shakes or checks) for reasons of aesthetics, economics and safety. With very few exceptions (these are described in Chapter 7), I see no particular merit in including such defects in a finished bowl. Splits and cracks are unpredictable and, although they might appear small in wet timber, could easily open as the wood dries. Moreover, they are always potential disasters—cracked timber spinning on the lathe can fly apart at any time.

Grain and stain Grain orientation may be manipulated on the lathe, but for the most part, the grain pattern you get in your bowl will depend on how you cut your log or board into bowl blanks. By

Elm bowls aligned as they were in the half log. Different bowl shapes can result in dramatically different patterns of sapwood and heartwood.

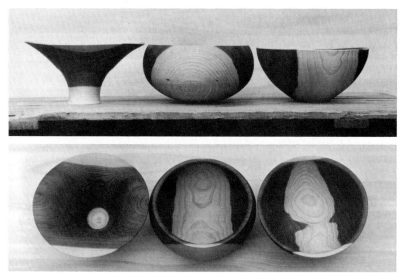

taking a good look at the way the grain runs along the length of a board or a log's surface and at the end grain, you can usually discern what lies within, and what hazards or joys might lie ahead.

If the bark is loose, remove it to see splits and signs of stress more readily. Note if the grain is straight, wavy, interlocked, twisted, or if there is anything else unusual, and try to project these irregularities into the wood. Take particular note of timber cut from a naturally stressed area of the tree. The distorted growth that occurs around crotches, burls, knots, or any place wood bends, usually indicates considerable tension and highly figured grain within. While these are likely to present problems of splitting and distortion, the results are often visually spectacular and might be worth the risk.

Logs that exhibit strong radial lines on their end grain, such as the oaks or casuarinas, also can be used to dramatic effect. Any surface cut parallel to these radial lines will reveal wide ribbons or flecks of ultra-smooth grain that contrast dramatically with the rest of the wood, which is typically coarse.

A jarrah burl, above, cut in 3-in.- (75mm) thick slices. Much of each slab is end grain, but the timber structure is so wild that this shouldn't affect the stability of the bowls.

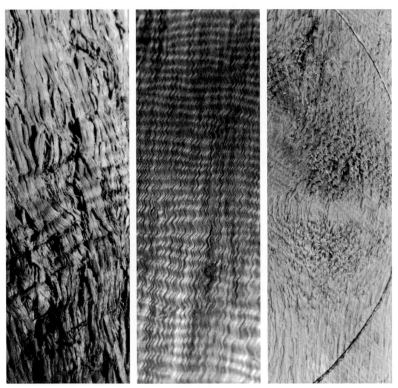

The bark's corrugations, far left, only hint at what lies beneath, center, and can easily be overlooked. At left, the areas of torn grain near the scribed circle indicate probable difficulties in cutting end grain cleanly.

Black-heart stain may run the length of a long sassafras log.

When this liquid-amber log was sliced, heavy spalting was revealed.

Black-heart stain, shown at far left, occurs in many species and usually originates from an injury sustained by the tree someplace up the trunk, which allows water to enter. Such staining is usually an early sign of decay.

In some cases, stain will take you by surprise. When I crosscut the end of the liquid-amber log at left to remove the end checks, I discovered heavy spalting within and a coloration far more varied and interesting than the creamy white I had anticipated. In many timbers, such as the blackwood acacia, shown on p. 23, the dramatic contrast between sapwood and heartwood is very desirable for waney-edged bowls.

Although metal always presents a danger to saws and other cutting tools, it can actually enhance timber by causing a chemical reaction to occur (see p. 142). Wood that has a high tannin content, such as oak or many of the eucalyptuses, will turn blue with even a short-term exposure to iron. Other woods will turn black or, in the case of English yew, a spectacular purple.

Logs to bowl blanks Bowl turners have several advantages over craftsmen in the rest of the timber trades, who are generally interested in seasoned boards or beams of good length and straight grain. Turners frequently work with green or semi-seasoned material, which also allows us to consider much smaller diameter trees that would never be sawn into boards. I strongly object to the common sawmilling practice of converting large-diameter trees to small-section boards. It is a waste of resources and an offense against the planet.

Instead of boards, the bowl turner should think in terms of square chunks or blocks, since this is the shape from which most bowl blanks are cut. There is no one ideal way to convert a log into bowl blanks. Your approach will depend on a number of factors, such as the size of the log, the shapes of the bowls you want to make and how soon you are going to turn the wood.

Because, when it is green, wood is easier to turn and there are fewer defects, I prefer to convert a log directly into roughed-out bowls as quickly as possible. If the log is in my workshop, I'll cut about six blanks at a time, and rough these on the lathe before preparing any more. These heavy bowl forms are set aside to dry and are finish-turned weeks or even months later, depending on the type of bowl being made. They will warp but rarely split. It is especially important to keep the grain of a rough-turned bowl symmetrical within the blank, or the bowl may warp so much that it will be impossible to turn true. (See Chapter 3 for more on rough-turning.)

If I have to transport the timber back to the workshop, the best solution is to cut the longest lengths I can handle, as shown in the photo on p. 15. This exposes a minimum of end grain, which can be coated with a wax sealer to reduce checking. (Various products are readily available through woodturning supply stores.) Sections are sliced off the log in multiples of the diameter of the bowls I hope to extract from that log. Figuring, for example, that a 13-in.-(330mm) dia. log will yield 12-in.- (305mm) dia. bowls, I usually cut lengths of 13 in. (330mm), 25 in. (620mm) and 37 in. (940mm) from the log. The extra inch added to each length accounts for slight end-grain checking and the width of the saw kerf as the discs are cut. (If you are unable to convert your log sections straight into roughed bowls, you should saw them into boards.)

Before you cut a log into bowl blanks, particularly an older log that has been felled for some time, you'll need to examine it carefully for the defects described above. Use a stiff brush to clean the surface and remove the dirt from small checks. I use a domestic scrub brush on relatively clean logs, and a heavy wire brush to remove thick mud and loose bark. A knife or a small plane or chisel will allow you to shave a clean, smooth surface to examine minute shakes or remove the oxidized surface to reveal the true color of the wood beneath. (A hatchet would serve the same purpose as well.)

After you've examined the end grain and long-grain surfaces of the log, take the smallest possible slice off the end of the log that shows the largest end-grain splits and defects. Examine the fresh cut to see which of the splits penetrates farther into the log. It is usually easier to examine the small off-cut face than the log itself. If this reveals defects that cannot be avoided, then the procedure must be repeated until they are gone. To seek out the smallest of checks, take the thin, off-cut slice of end grain and bend it slightly. Where there is a defect, the wood will crack or fold, rather than bend in an even curve. Use chalk or a lumber marker to identify anything you might fail to notice later.

How to cut? After cleaning the log, I figure out what I want by sketching bowl blanks on the end grain. During this planning stage, take into account any defects or irregularities; it is usually best to avoid the heart of the tree. The very tight growth rings at the center are prone to splitting, and will soon develop the notorious heart shakes shown in the photo at right. Besides splitting, the heartwood also will create a bump, or ridge, when it dries, as shown in the photos on p. 35.

Splitting is about average in this half log of elm, which was cut about six months before the photo was taken.

Broadly, there are three key ways of aligning a bowl blank within a log or board, as shown below. First, you can face the top and bottom of the bowl towards the end grain *(A)*. I do not recommend this alignment for anything other than small bowls, up to about 3 in. (75mm) dia., especially if the pith is included. Short end-grain fibers in the bottom of a bowl are so weak that a hard knock could easily punch a hole. Unless the wood is absolutely dry before you start, you run the added risk of splits across the bottom of your bowl if you retain the pith.

Second, you can place the bowl rim on the radius of the log, with the growth rings aligned at 90° to the top and base *(B)*. This quartersawn orientation is the least prone to warping. Looking at the bowl from above, as shown at the top of the facing page, you will see straight lines running across the base. These curve up the steep sides and can form "eyes" on opposite sides of the bowl if the form curves in at the rim. In profile, at center, the growth rings appear as straight lines on the end grain and *U*-shaped curves on the sides.

The third option is to face the top or base of the bowl towards the heart *(C)*, so that the growth rings lie roughly parallel to the rim of the bowl. This produces a flatsawn bowl with concentric rings in the bottom, as shown at bottom. In profile, the growth rings will be more or less horizontal on all sides.

In reality, however, you will seldom see such clear-cut grain alignment as in the samples at on the facing page, which were turned from fast-growing radiata pine. More often, you will be

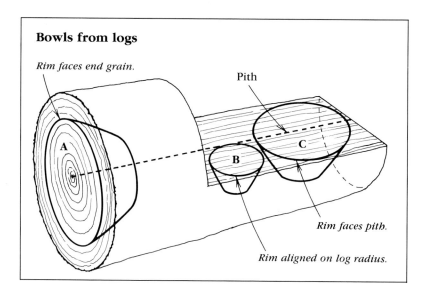

Bowls from logs

Rim faces end grain.

Pith

A

B

C

Rim faces pith.

Rim aligned on log radius.

At top and center are bowls made from
quartersawn blanks. In profile, these bowls
present different aspects. Growth rings
are strongly revealed on the end grain, but
are almost nonexistant on the side grain. At
bottom is a top view of bowls turned from
flatsawn blanks.

working with some twisted or distorted variation, which is usually far more spectacular and appealing. The sassafras and ash bowls below are more typical.

The photo at left on the facing page, shows a common (and ideal) bowl log. The off-center pith presents two options, which I've chalked on the end grain. Both follow the basic grain orientation shown at *C* in the drawing on p. 20—the top or base of the bowl will face the heart. (The concentric rings will be better defined if the base of the bowl faces the heart.) The option at left will yield two deep bowls, but these will warp very unevenly because of the off-center position of the heart. The right option, which will produce three bowl blanks, is better—the pith is centered in the blanks and the bowls should warp evenly.

A small, "buttressed" log, such as the blackwood acacia in the photo at right on the facing page, can be broken down in several different ways, as shown in the drawing on the facing page. At *A*, the growth rings are parallel to the base and will result in a pattern of concentric rings in the base. The left blank at *A* will produce a waney-edged bowl. The layout at *B* should result in several interesting rounded forms, with the lighter sapwood featured in broad bands on the outside. At *C*, the long length of log that must be cut to accommodate the large blank in the center will provide two of each of the smaller blanks. These should all display interesting splashes of sapwood.

Both of these large bowls make good use of heart-stained timber. The rim of the bowl at top is aligned towards the heart of the tree, but because the grain was not balanced in the blank, the center of the ring pattern is close to the rim in the foreground. In the bowl at bottom, the grain is reversed, with the base of the bowl facing the heart. The concentric rings are easily discerned near the rim, but get lost in the swirl of figured heartwood in the bottom.

You can take two different approaches to the off-center pith in this elm limb, below. The first option, at left, will provide two deep bowls, but these will warp unevenly due to the position of the pith. The right option is more symmetrical, and a much better bet. The "buttressed" blackwood-acacia log, below right, can be sliced in several different ways, which are shown in the drawing at bottom.

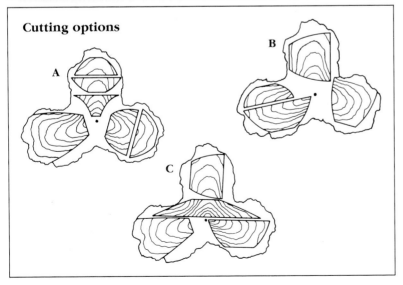

Cutting options

A

B

C

The sequence of photos at left on the facing page show the typical conversion of a small log into bowl blanks. I begin by highlighting the checks and defects on the end-grain slice. Next, I sketch out the possible bowl blanks with diagonal and cross-hatched lines. Then, using my hand as a measure, I transfer the maximum diameter from the end to the length of the log, and rip it in two on the bandsaw, sawing along the pith.

To cut a flat base parallel to the long (top) face of the blank, I must first cut one end at 90° to the long face, as shown at top right on the facing page. Then, I stand the blank on that end and cut the parallel surface. With that done, I am ready to cut a disc.

If the grain is not aligned in the blank as I might wish, there are ways of correcting the situation. The best time to make major adjustments is when the blank is squared on the bandsaw, and the removal of a wedge is easy. Trimming off angled wedges is simple if your saw has a tilting table. If it doesn't, use wedges to tilt and support the block at the desired angle. Once the blank has been sawn into a disc, it is quicker and safer to realign the grain on the lathe (see p. 98). But sometimes it's simply impossible to achieve symmetrical grain orientation, as in the jarrah burl shown on p. 17.

Boards to bowl blanks After the constant decision-making of log conversion, cutting discs from boards comes as light relief. By the time a log has been reduced to boards most of the decisions about grain alignment have been made. You are already committed. If you purchased the boards, you will have rejected unsuitable material, and you'll be anxious not to waste what you've already paid for.

Normally, I mark out my circles on a board using dividers, and cut out the discs using a bandsaw. This way I get squat cylinders and the freedom to create any form I want. But if I want to make several out-flowing forms on a small foot, I can get more out of my material by cutting the board as shown below. (I cut this board on

Cutting a board on the bandsaw for maximum return.

It takes two steps to cut a flat base parallel to the top face of an irregular blank. First, trim one end at 90° to the long face, top. Then stand the blank on that end and cut the parallel surface, bottom.

First, highlight any defects on the end grain, top, and sketch out the possible bowls, second from top. Then transfer the maximum bowl diameter to the length of the log, third from top. Finally, rip the log in two pieces along the pith, to the depth of the bowl blank.

the bandsaw, but it could also be done on a larger scale using a chainsaw—the angles aren't critical.) This is a great way to handle really expensive or unusual boards—I gain one extra bowl for every three cut conventionally.

Sometimes, I take a rather basic approach to achieve much the same end. To separate the small ebony bowl blanks in the photo on the facing page, I cut in from each face on the bandsaw, and then split the blanks apart between the sawcuts by holding one end of the board and bashing the other on the floor. Primitive, I admit, but more than effective in a situation where even a fine bandsaw blade cannot cut.

You can always make small bowls from the triangular offcuts between large bowls, as shown in the drawing on the facing page. A commercial point: I figure that the sale of small objects made from such offcuts should cover the cost of the whole board, and often much more. With my materials already paid for, the money I get from the sale of the primary pieces is icing on the cake. Since I've already covered my expenses with the offcuts, I feel less pressure to keep the price down on the primary pieces.

Saws for log conversion If you are going to convert your own logs into boards or bowl blanks you will need a bit of equipment. The bigger the logs the more you'll need, and that's when the real expense begins. But you should be able to acquire a good set of basic tools without spending too much.

Chainsaws A chainsaw is the essential tool when you're working with logs. There are masochists, heavily into the work ethic, who seem to enjoy the challenge of crosscutting and splitting out their boards by hand the hard way. But it's not for me—life is too short. There are both electric and gasoline-powered chainsaws on the market. If you expect to use your saw within range of an electrical outlet, I recommend investing in a good, small electric chainsaw and a long extension cord. My Makita electric chainsaw will cut through 13-in.- (330mm) wide stock, and has served me well for several years. I often wonder how I managed before, with only a larger gasoline saw. Electric saws have several advantages—they are lightweight, have no exhaust fumes and are relatively quiet, which makes it possible to use them indoors. My saw is not the cheapest on the market, but it's nowhere near the cost of the most expensive professional models, which I consider unnecessary for a small workshop.

Small chunks, like these ebony bowl blanks, were split apart after being cut in from opposite faces on the bandsaw.

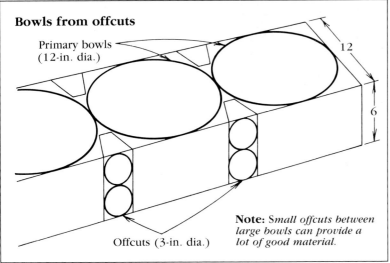

Bowls from offcuts

Primary bowls
(12-in. dia.)

12

6

Offcuts (3-in. dia.)

Note: *Small offcuts between large bowls can provide a lot of good material.*

Gas-driven saws come in all sizes—from the toys designed for domestic use, which don't really like to cut anything above 3-in. (75mm) diameter, to the powerful monsters used to decimate enormous trees. I've relied on a semi-professional, 65cc Husqvarna chainsaw for nearly ten years. I find its 18-in. (460mm) bar ideal and easy to handle, although the saw will accept a longer bar. If I have to cut logs that are larger in diameter than the bar length, I merely cut in from both sides. Even if I could cut larger logs, I probably couldn't move them anyway. I find both saws essential. I use the heavier Husqvarna for all work away from the workshop and electricity, as well as for cutting logs that are too big for the Makita.

Always remember that chainsaws can be dangerous. Handled carelessly, a saw can kick back into your face or body, fire chips into your eyes, or shoot splinters like darts. And saws are noisy. So:

- Never lean over a running chainsaw, even if it is just idling.
- Never leave a chainsaw running unattended.
- Always wear ear and eye protection or, better yet, a helmet that includes full ear and face protection.
- Make sure your saw is fitted with an automatic chain brake. (Most new models come with this feature.)
- Only the operator should be within arm's length of the saw.

If you've never used a chainsaw, get advice from a specialist on how to use it safely, or read one of the many books on the subject. These will also tell you how to maintain the machine and keep the chain sharp (an important key to safety).

Along with a chainsaw, there are a few other tools you'll want to include in your log-handling kit. I carry an ax, a splitting maul, wooden or plastic wedges (these won't damage your chain) and assorted crowbars and ropes. I usually wear heavy leather gloves for protection against splinters and venomous livestock, which in Australia are never too far away. And hard-toe safety boots or shoes are a must if you are using either an ax or chainsaw.

Before you cut your log, arrange it in a position suited to comfortable cutting and be sure that it is firmly secured. In the photos and caption on the facing page are several tips that will help ensure safe and efficient chainsawing. (Some turners use chainsaw mills to cut their own timber, but these represent a whole level of technology that I prefer to avoid. They are laborious, and I find I can rip short planks with a standard chainsaw whenever I need to.)

Bandsaws Bandsaws have two big advantages over chainsaws—a much thinner blade, and the ability to cut curves. Every bowl turner should have one. Using a good bandsaw, you can convert small logs

with very little waste. And the bandsaw's ability to cut tight curves will enable you to get the most out of your logs or boards.

Like chainsaws, there are all kinds of bandsaws on the market. There are flimsy models that might balk at cutting 1-in.- (25mm) thick boards and re-saw bandsaws that can slice a 36-in.- (915mm) dia. hardwood log with impunity. You need something in between.

The most important feature of any bandsaw that will be used to convert logs into bowl blanks is its depth of cut, which is the distance between the table and the blade guides. Look for a bandsaw with at least a 6-in. (150mm) depth of cut. It's even better to have a depth of cut that equals the approximate swing of your lathe (the maximum diameter you can turn). That way, you'll be able to use your bandsaw to pre-cut all the faces of the bowl blanks. If you intend to use your bandsaw only to cut discs from milled timber, you can get by with a smaller depth of cut than you'll need for cutting logs. A 4½-in. (115mm) depth of cut is adequate for most boards, but large discs or squares will have to be split with a chainsaw.

The throat on a bandsaw is the distance between the blade and the stanchion that supports the upper wheel. Although bandsaws are identified by their throat (a 14-in. saw has a 14-in. throat), this is less important than the depth of cut for most bowl turners. I use my bandsaw mainly to cut circles, and its 13¾-in. (350mm) throat is adequate because the bulk of a log or board can lie on the outboard side of the blade. If I need to cut longer lengths, I use a chainsaw or circular saw. A bigger throat is nice to have, however, and with

Make sure that a log is well supported before cutting, and avoid using metal or stone supports, which could damage your saw chain. Left: The log is blocked beneath and to one side of the point of cut, which ensures that the kerf won't close, pinching the sawblade as the cut progresses. When the log is cut through, the shorter length drops away from the support, opening the kerf. Center: Short offcut slabs wedge the curved underside of a log and keep it from rolling. Right: If you plan to cut a number of slabs from a single block, it is easier not to complete the cuts until the bulk of the sawing is finished.

most of the bandsaws that offer a large depth of cut—say, 12 in. (305mm) or larger—this is what you'll get. I am not fond of the saws that offer a very large throat—up to 24 in. (610mm)—but a shallow depth of cut—less than 6 in. (150mm). To obtain such a large throat, these machines have three wheels instead of two, which makes for awkward blade-tracking adjustments.

I have a good, small Startrite #352 bandsaw, which I bought mainly for its depth of cut. It can handle timber up to 11¾ in. (295mm) thick and has a 13¾-in. (350mm) throat.

In addition to the wide range of new saws on the market, there are a number of huge old industrial saws with 2-ft.- (610mm) to 3-ft.- (915mm) wide tables, and throats to match. These may stand seven to nine feet tall and often run on babbitt bearings. If you can handle the weight and have space in your shop, you could pick up a real bargain, but make sure that your shop has the power to drive such an animal before you take it home. You may need to replace the bearings, but it's probably well worth the effort.

With any bandsaw, make sure that there are escape routes for the sawdust. Many new saws are so well enclosed that the dust, particularly the long fibers produced by cutting along the grain of wet wood, is difficult to extract. You must be able to reach all parts of the saw easily, not only for cleaning but to change blades.

Bandsaw blades There are many different blades and you must have the right one for the job. Bandsaw blades are described by the number of teeth per inch. Smooth cuts require a fine blade with lots of teeth to the inch, rough cuts as few teeth as possible. Because I use the bandsaw primarily to rough-cut blanks from logs or discs from boards, I generally use blades with three or four teeth to the inch.

I've found that a ¼-in.- (6mm) wide blade will cut most 3-in.- (75mm) dia. discs with ease, while I use a ¾-in. (19mm) blade to mill boards up to the maximum width that the saw will allow. For most purposes, however, I use a ½-in. (13mm) blade, which handles discs of all sizes and cuts a reasonably tight curve. Using the bandsaw and these three blades in conjunction with my two chainsaws, I have yet to meet the log or board I couldn't handle.

The blade is tensioned around the wheels and it is inclined to twist slightly during cutting. This occurs particularly when cutting curves in thicker materials. On tough timber the blade can bow if not kept absolutely sharp. The blades I use cut well on all kinds of stock and, although they are considered disposable by the manufacturer, it is easy to regrind them, touching the top of the tooth lightly on a fine grinding wheel, as shown in the photo at right. As you grind the teeth back, you'll find that the ability of the blade to cut a tight circle diminishes. Nevertheless, typically I regrind up to ten times before the blade either wears out or, more often, breaks due to metal fatigue. (The quality of blade steel varies. Avoid the thin-gauge steels, usually shiny, in favor of the heavy-gauge, usually black in color.)

Blade guides   A bandsaw should not be regarded as a precision cutting tool, even when equipped with the best blade. All bandsaw blades have a tendency to wander, especially when cutting thick stock, but good guides should restrict this. There are several common systems, the best of which employ a small, ball-bearing-mounted wheel on each side of the blade and another to support the back of the blade and absorb any thrust. Your saw should have two sets of guides: one positioned just above the work on the end of an adjustable blade-guard post, the other just below the saw table.

Guards   All moving parts of the saw should be covered during operation, with only as much blade exposed as is required for the thickness of wood you are cutting. It is absolutely essential that the blade be contained should it come off the wheels or break while the saw is running. A surprising number of woodworkers use totally unguarded bandsaws, apparently oblivious to this danger.

Bandsaw safety   While statistics show that a bandsaw is not nearly as lethal an object as a chainsaw, it nevertheless should command a healthy respect.
- Be sure to study the manufacturers advice regarding the fitting and tracking of blades.
- Always stop the saw to adjust the guides.
- Position the upper guides as close as possible to the wood being sawn.
- Never leave the saw running unattended.
- Make sure your wood is properly supported.
- Never force your stock through the blade. If it's not cutting fast enough, it probably means that the wood is hard, the blade is dull, or you're in too much of a hurry.

Bandsaws and chainsaws are excellent, versatile machines. Just remember that inexperience, overconfidence and fatigue all contribute to the likelihood of an accident. As with any other power tool, you should pause before you use them to remind yourself that what you are about to do is potentially dangerous.

Regrind a bandsaw blade by touching each tooth's top lightly on a fine grinding wheel.

Always use an offcut to support your work when cutting on the bandsaw. There should be no space beneath the blade at the point where it enters the wood.

Rough-Turning and Seasoning

HEY were no fools, those old-time turners of decades past. Working away on primitive, man-powered lathes in the rural depths of Wales, Sweden, Korea, the Appalachian Mountains and elsewhere, they learned a thing or two. One of the more important things they knew was that wood is much easier to work when wet. You'd never catch them turning bowls from seasoned timber— it was far too much like hard work in an already too-harsh struggle to survive. The bowls warped a bit, but so what? They were cheap and serviceable. The Koreans even made a virtue of this distortion, although in other parts of the world bowls were sometimes re-mounted on the lathe and turned true.

With the introduction of mechanically powered machinery, wood-workers could bludgeon their way through the toughest material, losing sight of the advantages of working wood green, the sensible way. For the first two years of my turning career I never worked wet wood. The workshop where I learned the basics of my craft followed the normal trade practices of the time in England. Few turners rough-turned anything, even bowls, and it was hard work hollowing a large chunk of bone-dry teak, ash or elm. In the late 1960s and early 70s, it was still possible to go into a local sawmill and find stacks of both air-dried and kiln-dried timber suitable for bowls. I learned about rough-turning by accident. I was forced to use green wood after local supplies of dry timber had been bought up by con-tractors to make concrete building forms for new freeway bridges.

Small, roughed-out bowls distort as they season. This batch is ready to be remounted on the lathe and turned true.

Even at the best of times, large-section, well-seasoned boards suitable for bowls are difficult to find, and tend to be very expensive. And I prefer to leave them for cabinetmaking or other large-scale woodworking, rather than cut them up for bowl stock. If you want a supply of thick, dry timber, you'll probably have to cut your own, or order it specially. If you do, be prepared to invest a lot of time, money and space in the project.

These days, I carry very little seasoned stock for bowls, preferring the tried and tested bowl-roughing techniques. Aside from the ease of cutting, the major advantage of working wood when it is freshly felled is that waste will be minimal. Even small trees or branches, which would otherwise split if left to dry, can be used. An 8-in.-(200mm) dia. log should yield bowls of a slightly smaller diameter.

As I emphasized in Chapter 2, try to turn the wood before it even thinks of splitting and you'll get the most out of it. Of course, you'll pay a price for all this extra timber: You will get wet as the moisture is flung from the wood, and so will everything else in the firing line of the lathe. I wear a full set of waterproof raingear when I turn green wood. Some timbers, such as the oaks or eucalyptuses, have a high tannin content, and this will stain your hands black for a few days if you don't wear gloves.

Rough-turning The principle of rough-turning is to remove the bulk of the waste while the wood is easiest to work, and then to allow the roughly hollowed form to dry out before remounting it on the lathe to be turned true. The technique is straightforward, and should pose few problems.

Rough-turned bowls will distort as they dry, but tend not to split. Some of this movement is the result of altered tensions and stresses: A lump of wood reacts strongly, as might you or I, when you remove its guts. I plan on losing less than 5% through splitting, however, and I could avoid most of those losses if I took fewer risks and asked less of the material.

It is important to understand how the bowl is going to warp if you are not to lose it. If you cut bowl blanks willy-nilly from a log, you might lose the lot, either through splitting, or because the forms distort so much that, no matter how you remount them on the lathe, there won't be enough wood available for a complete bowl wall. At far right on the facing page is an example of just such a mistake. I have rough-turned, and later finished, thousands of bowls under a wide variety of climatic conditions. I take risks, often demanding far too much of the wood, usually in the hope of

Top left and center: Two views of a seasoned, rough-turned sassafras bowl. The warped ridge on the rim that is created by the heartwood when it dries can be turned away or incorporated into the design. Bottom left: The heart shake on this rough-turned bowl can be turned off without losing too much material, or the bowl could be turned thin and the splits detailed.

Below: A eucalyptus burl too eccentric to mount. I failed to align the grain symmetrically in the blank.

achieving some spectacular grain effect in a "one-off" gallery piece. But, for the run-of-the-mill food bowls that are my bread and butter, I play it safe by applying the guidelines described in Chapter 2, and lose very, very few.

When attaching a bowl to a faceplate for rough-turning, don't forget to use only two screws, aligned with the grain, as shown on p. 105. When the bowl shrinks across the grain, you will be able to remount it for finish-turning using the same screw holes. You will note that many of the roughed bowls shown in the photo on p. 33 have an internal shoulder. This is for remounting the bowl over the expanding jaws of a chuck to turn the outside (the first step in finish-turning).

I find that an even wall thickness of about one tenth of the bowl diameter will generally leave me with enough wood for a reasonable wall. It is better to err on the side of greater thickness. The evenness of the wall is as crucial as the quality of the timber. Variations in wall thickness will result in stresses that can cause the wood to split, and this applies equally to the base. From a 4-in. (100mm) by 12-in. (305mm) blank of a timber I know to be stable, I can usually rough-turn an 11½-in.- (295mm) dia. bowl, with a maximum wall thickness of ⅝ in. (15mm). For smaller bowls, I leave the wall slightly thicker—closer to one eighth of the bowl diameter, or about a ¾-in. (19mm) wall on a 6-in.- (150mm) dia. bowl. Small bowls seem to warp proportionally more than large ones, and the extra thickness gives me a little more material to work with.

If the grain or density of the wood varies a lot, or if the growth rings are not balanced symmetrically within the bowl blank, I increase the wall thickness to about one sixth of the diameter. This is usually enough to accommodate eccentric warping. For some of the chunkier bowls I like to make, I leave an even thicker wall (between one quarter and one third of the bowl diameter), but this presents a few problems. The thicker wall does not allow the bowl to move very much, so the wood tends to split instead. However, if a chunky, rough-turned bowl dries without major cracks or distortion, it usually requires very little final turning. Its very bulk gives it stability.

Seasoning There's an old rule of thumb for the length of time it takes to air-dry a board: one year per inch (25mm) of board thickness, plus an extra year. I prefer air-drying to any other method. Timber that has been properly air-dried has a working quality you will never find in kiln-dried material. Best of all to work are old hardwood beams. I have worked hundred-year-old oak, elm, ash and red-river gum and each was a joy, although harder to turn than green wood.

In my experience, the old rule of thumb is spot-on for boards, but not for roughed bowls. According to the formula, a 1-in. (25mm) wall thickness should require two years of seasoning. But I've found that most 16-in.- (405mm) dia. bowls with a 1-in.- (25mm) thick wall are stable after as little as two months, depending on the timber. This suggests that the warping of a rough-turned bowl may be partly due to the hollowing (which alters tensions within the wood), as well as to the drying, which is naturally quicker because of the increased end-grain surface. In practice, however, most of my rough-turned bowls lie around for a couple of years before they're used and replenished with new stock.

It's a good feeling to have hundreds of rough-turned bowls near completion, although it means that my design options are somewhat limited by my own stock. For example, a sudden market preference for thick bowls could present a problem if all the rough-turned bowls I have are thin. But I shall continue to rough-turn rather than season boards for the simple reason that a 6-in.- (150mm) thick board takes at least seven years to dry, a 4-in.- (100mm) thick board five. And I know from bitter experience that, even then, there is no guarantee that the wood won't warp when it's hollowed.

During the first few months of air drying, timber should be kept where a breeze can waft through it, and out of direct sunlight. Freshly sawn boards cut from wet logs must be separated to prevent discoloration and rot. They should be kept in level piles, stacked and separated by battens, or stickers, to keep them as flat as possible. After a minimum of six months, when the board surfaces are dry, you can remove the stickers until the drying cycle is complete. If a green board is stored on end, unrestrained by the weight of timber piled on top of it, it is likely to bow. However, because I am always looking for squares or discs, I stand my dried timber on end. This makes the timber much easier to handle. Weighty planks can be "walked" by pivoting the board first on one corner and then the other, in a rocking motion. And it's easy to balance even the heaviest board on its end while I assess it. To cut out bowl blanks, I simply flop the board down on two bearers, which raise it off the floor, and attack it with the chainsaw.

I keep rough-turned bowls in loose piles until their surface is dry, after which they go into slat-sided wooden crates salvaged from fruit and vegetable stores. After a few months they are transferred to

Freshly cut holly logs, stacked and drying in a shaded, well-ventilated shed.

cardboard boxes, where they can be forgotten for a year or two while they continue to dry more slowly. Once you have a store of roughed bowls and the drying cycle is under way, this system works well.

If you want to induce spalting in your timber, then forget all this and keep your timber in damp, poorly ventilated conditions. Not only will spalted timber be discolored, frequently it will have highly decorative patterns of black lines and assorted blotches. People are now experimenting with methods to induce and control various types of spalting, and who knows what pretty patterns they might achieve. But you should remember that spalt is another word for incipient rot. Spalted wood will not be in prime condition, and is therefore of questionable durability. For this reason, I avoid using it. (See Chapter 7 for more on spalting.)

Kiln-drying is the preferred method of commercial seasoning today. It is much faster than the traditional, air-drying process, and more suited to modern production needs in the furniture and building trades. While much of the timber available now is kiln-dried, it is rarely large enough for bowl blanks. This is mostly for economic reasons: Drying boards up to 2 in. (50mm) thick is relatively quick, easy and inexpensive. Boards 3 in. (75mm) thick take weeks longer, and the higher costs lessen their demand. Boards 4 in. (100mm) thick take months to kiln-dry and are prohibitively expensive.

Apart from the expense, there is another, more important reason I do not use kiln-dried timber. Often there are chemical additives used in the kiln-drying process to kill fungi or otherwise aid preservation, and these cannot be good for anyone's health. I had a bad experience with a couple of batches in the mid-1970s that I hope never to repeat.

If you're still not convinced, consider what happened with my first batch of rough-turned bowls. I was in a rush to fill an order, so I put them through the local kilns. All looked fine at first, with just a little twisting and no splits. But as I began to turn the first one true, I uncovered a mass of honeycomb shakes just below the surface, and this proved to be the case in more than half the bowls. It was an expensive experience, the result of having rushed the kiln-drying process. These bowls had been placed in the kiln with a quantity of lumber that required less time. Undaunted, I tried another kiln, and, although the results were better, the waste was still unacceptable. Fortunately, I never needed to use kiln-dried timber again—soon after, I had amassed a large enough stock of rough-turned bowls to supply my future orders.

Microwave seasoning   Almost as soon as microwave ovens first got into our kitchens there were attempts around the world to use them for seasoning small pieces of wood, especially turned bowls. I, along with many others, was taken with the idea and found it to be a winner. But I find it works only if the bowls are very thin. As a standard procedure for drying rough-turned bowls, I do not consider the technique worthwhile. It is too inefficient. Conventional microwave ovens do not seem effective in penetrating more than 1 in. (25mm) of wood thickness. While a green-turned, 6-in.- (150mm) dia. bowl with a ⅛-in. (2mm) wall thickness can be dried to a crisp in about two minutes, one of similar diameter with a ⅝-in. (15mm) wall requires up to six minutes to get hot. It takes several more sessions in the oven—each a few minutes long, with a cooling-off period between them—to get it dry. I find all of this rather tedious and I've had no success at all in drying large, rough-turned bowls (12 in. [305mm] or larger, with a 1-in. [25mm] wall). But as a tool for distorting thin decorative bowls, I love it!

Polyethylene glycol   PEG has been promoted widely as the ultimate solution for preventing shrinkage in timber. And so it is if you chop your tree down and stick it straight into a vat of the stuff for a few months. It works by replacing the bound water in the wood with the chemical. As the wood dries, the PEG supports the cell walls and maintains the bulk and form of the timber, making it semi-plastic. What's more, being hygroscopic, PEG will attract moisture from the air. If the treated timber is not absolutely saturated with water to begin with, PEG will cause it to absorb more. And once all the water has been replaced with PEG, the timber can still exchange moisture with the air unless it is sealed completely—that means without even the merest pin prick.

I have never used PEG because so many professionals I've talked to over the years have tried it and found it unsatisfactory for bowl making. The process of curing with PEG takes about as long, it seems, as for air-drying, and your finishing options are much more limited because of the need to seal the wood completely.

Form

AFTER the colors have faded and the grain patterns have become obscure, only the form of a bowl will ensure its survival as a desirable object. A bowl of spectacular color or grain will draw gasps of admiration regardless of its shape, but this is no indication of how good a bowl it is. It is the *timber* that is being praised, not the bowl. While it is all very well to use grain and color to stunning effect, these characteristics will never outlast the shape—the most important aspect of a bowl.

Form is all too often regarded in visual terms only. But because bowls are also handled, the tactile qualitites are just as important. It is exceedingly difficult to make a bowl that is a pleasure to handle and invites a hand to explore the subtlety of balance between the mass of its base and rim. All this in an object that must look good, too!

Woodturning always involves curved surfaces. You can't avoid them on a lathe and, unless you confine yourself to turning cylinders and cones, you'll soon find yourself contemplating the subtleties of curves that arc smoothly through several planes.

This chapter is about curves. I will begin by considering them in their simplest form—as represented by a single line. Curves are curves, so I want to discuss them in the abstract before suggesting how to apply them to the profile of a bowl, or how they might relate to one another. For the time being, forget the lathe and the roundness it can impart to the simple curve of a profile.

Banksia, 10½-in. (270mm) diameter, turned green and microwaved.

Any line that is not straight is curved. That said, a lot of curves can be pretty subtle. But what is a curve, besides a bent line? It does not have any kinks, flat spots or abrupt changes in direction. You should be able to feel along a curve without discerning anything other than a smooth transition of altering direction, a pleasure we must all have experienced in our lives when fondling a smooth object such as a pebble, a teacup or a warm body. The slightest bump or dip mars the smoothness and jars your senses.

Let's start with two simple curves. The first, and most obvious, is an arc drawn with a compass. The tightness of the curve is dictated by the radius of the circle of which it is the circumference. The second is the catenary curve formed by a flexible chain hanging between two points. As you can see from the photos below, no matter where the ends are in relation to one another, the curve is smooth and symmetrical. There are numerous examples of catenary curves all about us—power lines, bead necklaces, chains across

The photos at top and center, when rotated 90° clockwise, illustrate good enclosed bowl forms.

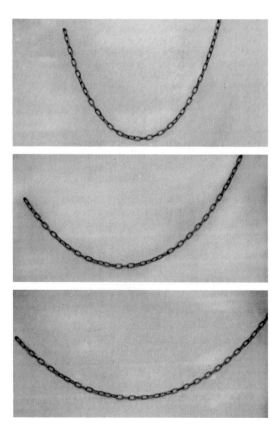

driveways, etc. These open curves are subject to basic laws of mechanics and gravity and are uncompromising in their symmetry. But rotated 90°, the photos at top and center on the facing page, in particular, become more interesting and suggest possible bowl forms.

One of the best ways of seeing what you can achieve with asymmetry is by playing around with a flexible rod, as shown in the photos below. The length of plastic-coated curtain wire illustrates that the line flows easily, however I tighten or extend the curve. These are all simple curves, where the bend continues in one direction. But in the photo at bottom right, pressure exerted on the ends of the curtain wire creates an *S*-bend. Still, the line flows smoothly.

We rarely see curves in isolation, however, since they are more often applied to three-dimensional objects. Similar curves occur frequently in nature, where they are smooth and always arc evenly. Keep your eyes and mind open. Assess what you are looking at and, if you see a curve you feel strongly about, try to define why.

Bent curtain wire curves gradually and without any flat spots or kinks to mar the flow of the line.

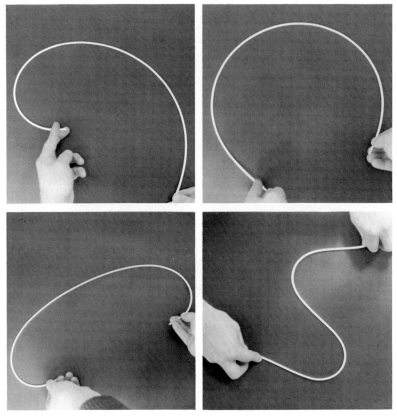

Fluid, ever-changing curves occur throughout the living world, alongside man-made curves.

Where might you look for inspiration? Note the way gravity acts upon a slender structure held at one end, such as a blade of grass or the curve of the palm fronds shown at left. Your own kitchen is full of other interesting curves: pears, avocados, butternut squash, and so on. The landscape is another excellent place to look. In the photo at bottom left there are a number of curves—both natural and man-made. The road sweeps around before the rounded hill, the form of which is revealed by light and shadow. In the left foreground, the gravel curves away from the white line. During the heyday of the Arts and Crafts Movement many wonderful forms were drawn directly from nature, or based upon shapes spawned by the Industrial Revolution. In urban areas look closely at buildings, especially the older ones that sport arches or towers.

Farther from the madding crowd, I find inspiration in windblown sand dunes and snowdrifts, or in the curl of an ocean swell breaking on a flat beach. I am fascinated by sensual curves such as these and I try to recreate them in my bowls. And then there are always bodies—of cars and of people. For those who don't care to loiter around the streets gazing at bodies for fear of being arrested, there are magazines full of all the raw material you could ever want.

Proportion

Certain proportions have always had universal appeal. Museums provide abundant evidence that throughout all generations and in all civilizations, similar proportions recur in artifacts and structures. These divisions of space and form rest well on the eye. The use of such proportion can lend an object the kind of presence exemplified in the Taj Mahal or in a fine Japanese tea bowl.

Some people are fortunate to have a built-in sense of proportion and are able to apply this without apparent effort to their work. For those of us who are less well-endowed, there have been a number of attempts over the years to define the ideal division of space and form. These generally involve complex mathematical formulae, which I will summarize only briefly, since there are great tomes analyzing each system in depth.

Perhaps the most widely known formula is the Golden Mean (or Golden Section) rectangle, which was devised by the Ancient Greeks. In this idealized rectangle, the ratio of the short to long sides is 1:1.618, which can be derived through several mathematical progressions and geometrical figures. (Leonardo Fibonacci, the 13th-century Italian mathematician, developed a progression of numbers in which each number is the sum of the two before it: 1.1.2.3.5.8.13.21.34.55.89, and so on. If you divide the number 8, or any number above it, by the number that immediately precedes it, the value approximates that of the Golden Mean.)

The Golden Mean rectangle is easily constructed and can be subdivided to provide smaller rectangles of similar proportions. To form a Golden rectangle geometrically, construct a square *abcd*, as shown below. Using *m* as the midpoint of *cd* and the center of the radius *mb*, draw an arc to cut the extended line *cd* at *f*. Then complete the rectangle *aefd*. The ratio of *fc:cd* is 1:1 618. To split any length in similar proportions, simply divide the length by 1.618. Multiply any length by 1.618 to ascertain the larger portion of the ratio. For example: 3 x 1.618 = 4.85, or the ratio 3:4.85.

Problems of proportion recur constantly in bowl turning. The most basic are the ratio of the diameter to the height of a bowl blank and the diameter of the base to that of the rim. Using a calculator, these can be resolved easily according to the Golden Mean (although we are usually too busy getting the most out of our logs or boards, or meeting the needs of whatever chucks or other fixings we have on hand).

Once the overall proportions have been established, you have to figure out how to divide the horizontal spaces within a bowl's profile: How high should the foot be? Where should decorative beads or grooves be placed on the rim of a thick-walled bowl? These masses can be divided according to the Golden Mean, or you can use more basic proportions, such as 1:3 or 1:4. I find that the key is

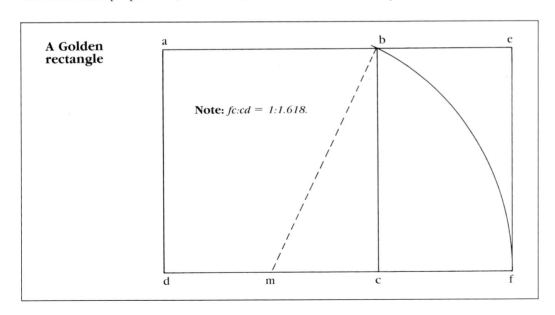

A Golden rectangle

Note: *fc:cd = 1:1.618.*

to be none too exact or the result will look contrived, but there are a few basic and generally accepted guidelines. A mass divided in two will look better if the parts are unequal, as shown at *A* in the drawing below. Three unequal masses should be stacked in order, with the largest on either top or bottom, *B*. But if two of the masses are equal, *C*, the third should lie between them. Drawing *D* shows that when equal subdivisons are together at the bottom, the mass looks top-heavy. If you want to use three or more horizontal divisions it is best to divide the primary mass into three parts and then subdivide each part using the same guidelines.

I try to bear all this in mind as I turn or design a form, and there are many applications of these abstract principles throughout this book—particularly in the following section on profiles. Unfortunately, rigid adherence to such rules of proportion is no guarantee of success. They should be regarded as guidelines, which will aid your confidence and stimulate your perception of the possibilities—not limit them. Your art is your personal sense of the arrangement of space and mass.

Profiles The profile of a bowl is of preeminent importance. It is usually the first part to be turned and is the surface to which the rim and inside relate. The quality of the profile always dictates the quality of the bowl; whether you distort the rims or smother the form with beads

Proportion

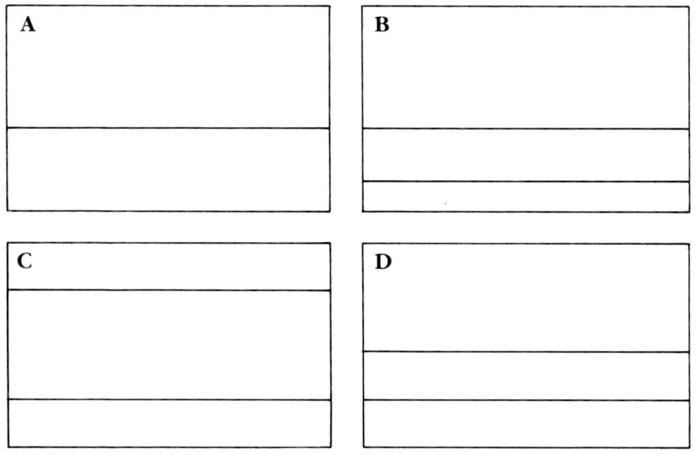

A

B

C

D

and coves, the basic curves and proportions always show through these embellishments. Good basic form is vital, and, while in an abstract sense any curve is a good curve, how you apply any portion of that curve (or curves) will make the difference between your bowl looking good, bad or downright ugly. How you might combine and use curves is the major concern of this book.

Between the (usually) horizontal and parallel planes that describe the rim and base of a bowl, the side can follow any line you choose—from a simple parabolic curve to some bizarre combination of beads, coves, grooves and other assorted bits of turning virtuosity. All bowls fall into one of the three main categories: open, closed or cylindrical. (The straight-sided forms present problems of proportion only.) The variations are infinite, although relatively few will really satisfy the eye or give the groping hand a thrill.

The challenge of trying to achieve the right curves in the right proportions continues to fascinate craftspeople in all media. Potters tell me that the beginning and end of a curve are what count; get these right and you can get away with anything in between. While there's an element of truth in that assertion, I don't agree with the latter part at all. I've started and finished some curves right, and then made a complete mess in between with the greatest of ease!

No matter how near to perfection one solution might seem, it is always possible to find ways in which the form might work even better. It never ceases to amaze me how, over thousands of years, generations of potters, metalworkers and glassblowers all over the world have gravitated towards similar bowl forms. I have seen Inca bowls that were made around fifteen hundred years ago, which are almost identical to ones made in Egypt at about the same time. Bowls of the New and Old Worlds appear to spring from similar traditions.

After a few thousand years of human endeavor, I can't help but feel that it all has been done before. In the following pages you are unlikely to find an original form. I might feel that I developed many of them myself, but they are almost certainly variations of well-worn themes. Much of my inspiration comes from ceramics, particularly those of Japan, Korea and the Middle East, and I am sure this is reflected in many of my bowls.

In the rest of this chapter, I have assembled a variety of shapes to be explored and refined. They are not meant to be the definitive solution to any problem, but rather a starting point. Study the profiles and try to understand their underlying principles. Then go to the lathe and see what you can come up with. Trust your eye and check the measurements only if things look drastically wrong. At the end of the next chapter are a number of profiles you can use to make templates, which will help you reproduce the forms and understand them better.

The foot Before considering the bowl profiles, I must mention the foot—a common element to all kinds of bowls. The word *foot* is used to define any secondary mass that supports the primary mass of a bowl. A foot is a great device for getting some lift and life into a profile. Feet come in all shapes and sizes (as usual) but fall in two general catagories. The simplest foot flows into the primary mass of the bowl, as shown at left in the photo below, lending visual thrust to the form, especially in outward-flowing bowls. In such cases, it may be hard to tell where the foot ends and the bowl begins, because of the way one curve flows into another. The second type of foot, on the bowl at right in the same photo, is a separate entity— neither the foot nor the bowl will stand well on its own, although they work quite nicely together. If the bowl profile flows on through the foot, as in drawings *A*, *B* and *C* on the facing page, the overall form is better balanced than in *D*, where the projected lines of the sides intersect below the base, making the form a trifle heavier visually.

Steeper, asymmetric curves are handled differently. The base of the foot should rest where the line of the profile intersects the horizontal plane on which the bowl sits, as in *E* and *F*. At *G*, the corner created by the abrupt change of direction in the wall lies on the line between the rim and foot. As with all other proportions, these are not hard and fast rules, but are guidelines to be absorbed into the subconscious and adhered to only roughly.

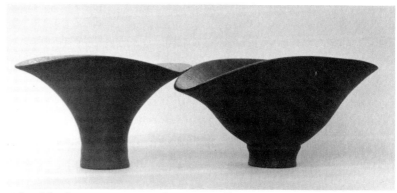

A foot lifts the primary mass of the bowl off the table.

Footed forms

Open forms All the curves in this section flow outward, occasionally nearing the vertical, but seldom crossing that line to return toward the center of the bowl. Simple convex or concave curves can be used individually, or combined to create ogees, or S-shapes. But remember that the outward sweep of a concave curve, which creates a mood of generosity, can be marred if the profile turns back towards the rim.

An arc is the simplest of curves and will produce the simplest profile. In the drawings at the left on the facing page you can see in the half-profiles the effect of three different arcs. At *A*, the center of the arc (*cp*) is at the center of the rim. The arc sweeps away from the base well enough, but arrives at the rim to leave me with a sense of unfulfilled promise. It looks like it was cut off in its prime, before it could run its full course.

At *B*, the center of the arc has been lowered to enable the curve to return slightly at the rim. The rim is much better, but the bottom of the curve is a disaster area—the base has broadened to make the form exceedingly stodgy. This is a very common bowl profile, usually resulting from the strictures of an expanding collet chuck or an oversized faceplate.

The solution is to use a tighter arc with its center below the rim, as in *C*. This works quite well. The diameter of the base is approximately two-fifths the diameter of the bowl, and the profile bounces in slightly from the fullness of the curve, making the form more restful to the eye. It will also feel better in the hand than either of the others.

The top profile in the drawing at right on the facing page is based on a circle and the Golden Mean. The diameter, height and base are related in the 1:1.618 ratio—(base : height), (height : diameter), (base + height = diameter). As a 6-in.- (150mm) dia. bowl with a ½-in. (6mm) wall, this form would be generous for side salads or breakfast cereals. The fullness of the arc gives a generous form, while the return of the curve hints at containment and reassures us that any wayward contents will be kept inside the bowl by the rim.

Even though this profile looks good, I find it dull next to the asymmetric curve shown in the bottom profile in the same drawing, which is of the same overall dimensions. The shallow curve at the base springs more dynamically from the flat surface before it tightens near the rim. This creates interest around the fullness of the curve, while still offering a sense of containment and of a curve resolved. I regard this form highly and have made thousands of bowls with this shape.

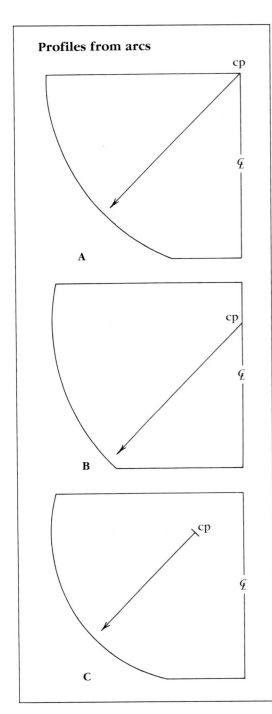

Profiles from arcs

A

B

C

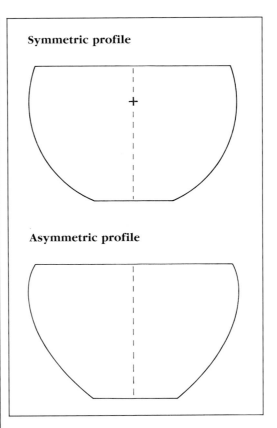

Symmetric profile

Asymmetric profile

In the photos below are two of the thousands of production salad bowls I have made. The top example was photographed from below to show the angle at which the curve of the bowl side meets the table. The other was shot from a slightly higher position to reveal the flat rim and to show how the bottom of the curve melts into the shadow around the base. This makes the form somewhat indecisive, perhaps even mysterious, and lends a floating quality to each bowl.

The bowl at left in the photo on the facing page is one of my favorites. It has a delicate curve, which becomes even more subtle near the base but is never a straight line. The power of the curve rises directly from the table. By contrast, the bowl on the right is dull, killed by the hard, straight line rising from the base. Had its maker maintained even the slightest curve on the lower section, its profile would have been equal to that of the bowl on the left.

Top: Ash, 13-in. (330mm) diameter. Bottom: Teak, 18-in. (455mm) diameter.

Only very little difference in the curve separates the fine bowl, at left, from a near miss, at right. The bowl on the right is deadened by its flat lower profile. When it was freshly turned, it was redeemed by its spectacular grain and color, which have since faded to dull yellow.

In the series of asymmetric curves below you can see how the location of the tightest part of the curve affects the form. The position of the curve in relation to the rim and base is largely responsible for our gut reaction to a bowl's form. With the tightness of the curve near the rim, as in *A*, there is a sense of anticipation: Here is a bowl that will contain well. As the tight curve moves down the side, in *B*, a different feeling is generated. The form is more open as the curve sweeps out to the rim after a tight beginning. Whatever was lost in the sense of containment is offset by the sheer generosity of the form, yet it still conveys a sense of security regarding its function as a container.

As the tight curve descends further, in *C* and *D*, the form begins to sag. Such forms can sometimes be rescued, however, by the addition of a foot. At *CC*, the 25° angle is steep enough to allow an abrupt reversal into the foot, although the actual tightness of that curve is disguised and softened by the addition of two beads. The line of the curve flows through the beads, with the slightly smaller lower bead enhancing the upward thrust of the profile.

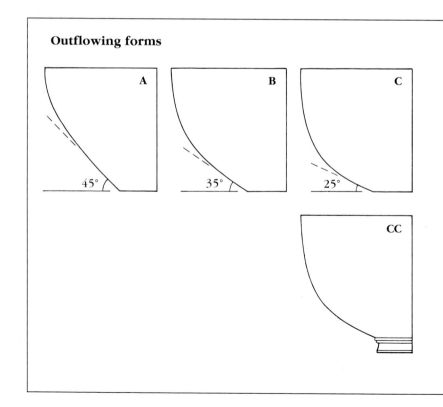

Outflowing forms

Because the curve of *D* lifts off at only 15°, I have popped form *DD* up on a cylinder. The upward thrust of the asymmetric curve on the foot makes no attempt to flow into the primary mass, but merely supports it. The bead softens the otherwise stark transition from vertical to horizontal.

The profile at *E* is beyond hope—the long shallow curve that created the lift in *A* does not work at all when reversed. If the base has to be this wide to accommodate your faceplate or chuck, you should choose another form.

In such deep forms, the ratio of the height to the diameter demands that the curve rise steeply over a short distance, even on a small base. It is important to place the tightest part of the curve in the upper two-thirds of the wall. As a general rule, the curve should set off from the base at no less than a 35° angle, as in *A* and *B*. This should satisfy any subliminal anticipation inspired by an upward thrusting line. If the curve leaves the base at an acute angle and tightens too quickly, the form will look slumped and heavy.

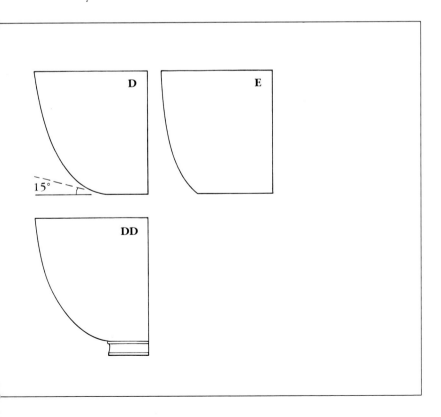

The 10-in.- (255mm) dia. elm bowl at right is lifted nicely by a simple cylindrical foot. The bowl at far right, made by Ivan Hollis of Batemans Bay, Australia, is a rare example of a successful, goblet-like form.

On the bowl at left above, the foot lifts the primary form visually as well as physically. The bowl at right sits on a tall, stem-like foot with an elegance rarely seen in such forms.

In a shallow outflowing form, where the emphasis is on an outward rather than an upward flow of line, the tightest part of the curve is still best kept near the rim. In the series of profiles on the facing page, you can see that a steeper line at the base will create a heavier look. The acute angle at which the curve meets the flat surface in *A* and *B* gives the form its floating quality. In *C*, the tightest part of the curve tucks into the base to create a slightly slumped appearance.

Once again, a foot will make quite a difference in the impact of the form, although I don't think that *A* and *B* gain very much by the addition since they already work pretty well. Below each of the profiles at far right are three standard variations. In each, the upper variation provides a solid base for the primary mass. The middle variation is lighter and leads the eye up and away from the base. In the bottom variation, the foot is too wide and makes the angle between the curves of the foot and the wall too acute.

The bottom foot at *AA* has a thin edge, which is too fragile. It can be thickened, as at *BB*, but this makes the whole foot too heavy for the upper mass of the bowl. A similar foot works better in *CC* because of the shallower curve that rests upon it—the heavier look of the curve demands more support. The middle solution for *CC* looks less stable, but imparts a good lift to the bowl.

The upward thrust of the curve at *D*, combined with its tightness near the base, makes for a turgid form. The curve at *E* springs from the same point and is similar to the one at *B*, but it doesn't work as well on the squatter form because the thrust is more up than out. As you can see in *DD* and *EE*, the addition of a foot does little to lighten the form; rather it seems to emphasize the chunkiness.

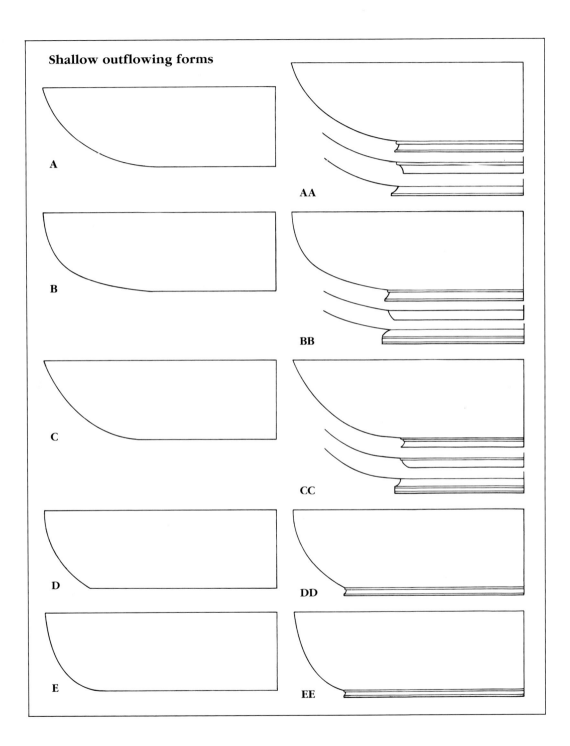

Shallow outflowing forms

A

AA

B

BB

C

CC

D

DD

E

EE

Until now, all the profiles have rested on flat bases or feet, and one of my favorite forms—the rounded bottom—hasn't been considered. Below is one of my well-used Irish-elm salad bowls. The curve of its profile flattens out on the bottom to provide a reasonably steady base, although any flat base will eventually warp, causing the bowl to wobble. Such forms are the very essence of bowl— all round and tactile. And they function well—they might rock a little, but they can't tip over.

Concave curves I find concave curves even more difficult to handle well. Proportions are vital if a form is to have a floating quality, without looking either too squat and stubby or so light and finely balanced that a puff of wind might blow it away. In the profiles in the drawing on the facing page, you can see the real superiority of an asymmetric curve over an arc. I find the predictable arcs at *B* and *D* mundane, compared to the dynamic, asymmetric curves at *A* and *C*. The latter spring to life. Their profiles take off steeply through the tightness of the curve before sweeping outwards (creating an integrated foot in the process). Such curves hint at infinity, heading

Irish elm, 15-in. (380mm) diameter, inspired by the old English dairy bowls.

Each form narrows slightly above the base before sweeping out to the rim, demonstrating the strength of an asymmetrical curve. Queensland rosewood mahogany, 8-in. (200mm) diameter.

Symmetric and asymmetric concave curves

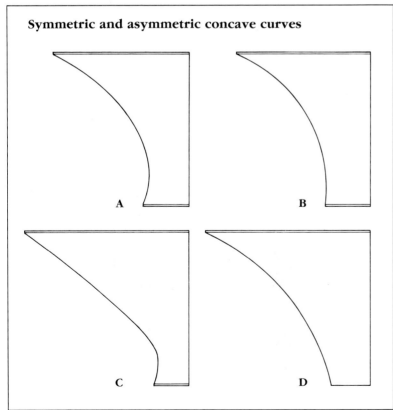

A

B

C

D

This 6-in. (150mm) bowl just misses being an exhibition-quality piece. The curve flattens out too much, disrupting the flow.

into space on a trajectory, like Halley's comet. The profile of the bowl at left falls just short of achieving this effect. The center of the curve flattens slightly to interrupt the sense of motion.

These asymmetric curves look good in shallower forms, such as the ones at left in the drawing below, although they level off too much at the rim, diminishing the sense of the infinite. I rarely employ concave curves on thick-walled bowls. Their whole nature implies lightness and fragility, and the thin rims associated with such forms are particularly vulnerable.

The concave curves work well on stubbier forms, such as the ones at right in the drawing below, when you are committed to a wide, flat base—although the rim on *D* is too thin to be practical. These shapes work much better than the stubby, convex curves at the bottom of p. 57. They not only look better, they function better, too, being easier to lift and hold. There is little benefit from having a distinct foot, since the curves thrust forcefully off a flat surface and create their own integrated foot.

The line of the profile can be rolled right over at the rim, as shown in the drawing on the facing page, but you should avoid creating too tight a curve as in *B*. The rim overhangs the wall too much and is likely to be out of balance. *A* is better; the form is more open and generous. The overhanging rim works best on a larger scale, however, as shown at *C*. In the photo on the facing page, a similar rim provides an opportunity to create a dramatic piece.

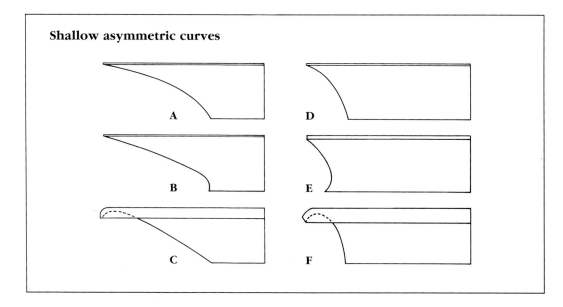

Shallow asymmetric curves

A

B

C

D

E

F

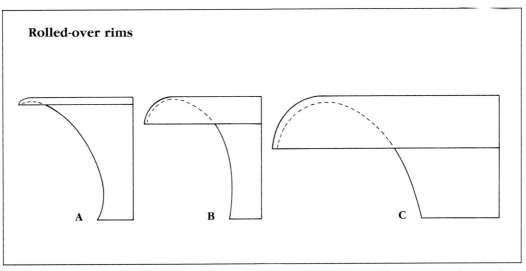

Rolled-over rims

A

B

C

This 8-in.- (200mm) square bowl, made by Vic Wood of Melbourne, Australia, exploits the potential of an overhanging rim.

Complex, outflowing ogees will arouse a similar set of visual perceptions. But things are more complicated as curves combine to flow one into another. The form is too heavy if the line moves away at too shallow an angle from the surface on which it sits. An ogee rarely sits that well on its own—it needs to be lifted off the surface.

In the profiles below, you can see the difference a return curve at the base of *B* can make to form *A*, which does not otherwise sit happily. The ideal is a curve that springs off the flat surface, as in the bowl on the facing page. The narrow foot rises steeply from the surface, and the profile continues to flow upward and outward.

The drawing on the facing page again illustrates the importance of the position of the tightest part of the curve—this time with an ogee-shaped profile. But there are more places to go wrong here than with the simple curves shown on pp. 54-55. An ogee can combine drastically different curves—tight little curls with long almost-flat arcs, or identical reversed curves. The options are limitless. At *A* is a good basic form: The tight arc of the foot flows into the full portion of the curve and reverses to create a shallow arc, which flows out and up in a wonderful open form. This arc can be extended, as at *B*, to create a much larger bowl before the curve drops below the horizontal line of the rim. And you can cut it off at almost any point and still have a good curve.

The same cannot be said about the other profiles in this group. Profile *C* suffers from a weight problem—the curve sags and the base is too wide and the foot mean. The foot and lower curve of *D* are better, but it is too full on the rapid reverse to the rim. The upper curve needs to be shallower, as at *E*, to eliminate the quirkiness. The initial descent from the rim in *E* is fine, but the reverse is not quite full enough, which makes the curve into the foot too long. The top half of *E*, in combination with the bottom of *D*, would make a good bowl. The dotted lines show how each form can be improved.

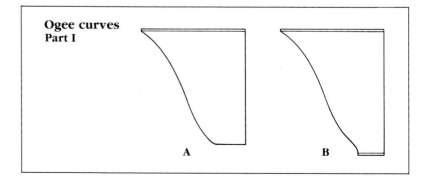

**Ogee curves
Part I**

A   B

The foot makes an important contribution to this 8-in. (200mm) holly bowl, by lifting its elegant ogee curve off the surface.

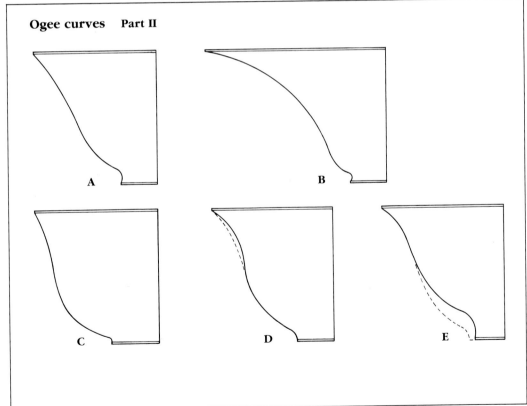

Ogee curves   Part II

A

B

C

D

E

If an asymmetric curve reverses and tightens too quickly, especially near the rim, it is easy for the form to become trite. Below are a couple of examples—the upward thrust is halted and weighed down somewhat by the heavy rim. If the basic curve is good you'll get a nice bowl, but nothing really exciting.

In the series of profiles on the facing page, the ogee is applied to a shallow form. Profiles *A*, *B* and *C* work well with a foot. Each primary mass sits nicely on its plinth, flowing generously outwards. Profile *A* would make a practical serving bowl where extra stability is required. Profiles *B* and *C* are much more elegant, but less practical, unless the wall is left thick. The long, out-flowing line lifts the form beautifully, making each ideal for a thin-walled bowl.

Profiles *D*, *E* and *F* are unsatisfactory, but not without merit. In each case, the curve that forms the foot doesn't quite work. The height of the foot in *E* (indicated by the arrow) is too great in relation to the primary mass, lending it an unbalanced air. The same is partly true for *D*, but its wider base and steeper curve create a profile of uninspiring chunkiness. In a good, safe solution such as *F*, the plain foot is stark, and could be replaced by a beaded foot like one of those in *A*, *B* or *C*.

The wide, shallow profiles *G* and *H* present two excellent solutions to lifting the primary mass while maintaining stability in a bowl of these proportions. The outward thrust of the foot in *G* and *H* prepares the eye to follow the outward flow of the upper curve to the rim. By contrast, *I* is very stubby and inelegant.

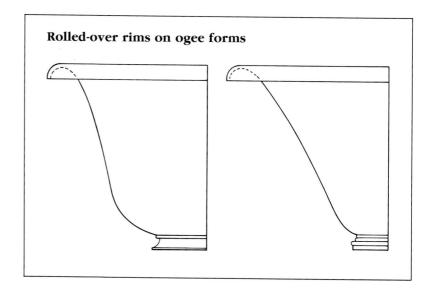

Rolled-over rims on ogee forms

Shallow ogee curves

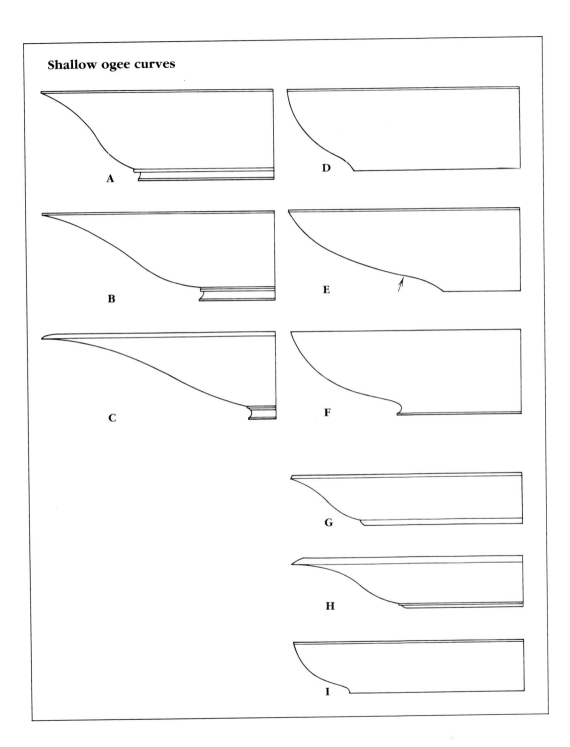

A

B

C

D

E

F

G

H

I

Closed forms In each profile in this section the rim is narrower than the width of the bowl. These are containing, even secretive forms.

The top row of the series below shows five strong forms with the fullness of the curve at different heights. The diameter of the base of each is about three-quarters the diameter of the bowl—roughly the Golden Mean. These profiles, particularly *B* and *C*, will also work on much wider bowls of the same height, although on a larger scale the results tend to be safe rather than inspiring.

In profile *A*, the long, shallow curve away from the flat surface leads the eye upwards before turning back to the rim. This form still offers the contents almost as well as do the outflowing shapes, while *B*, *C* and *D* enclose the bulk of the contents deep in the form's belly. Salad bowls shaped like *B*, *C* and *D* are always popular because the contents are easily tossed and contained. But all the interesting heavy bits of radish, fruit and lizard biltong sink to the bottom and hide beneath the lettuce. I prefer the more open shapes for dining. Form *E* is a practical food bowl with good visual lift.

In the lower row, *AA* through *DD*, are some common variations. All suffer from too wide a base and from having the tightest part of the curve in the wrong place. The steep curve generates no lift to the form and would be greatly improved by sweeping into a narrower base. My rule of thumb for functional forms of this nature is that the base diameter be no more than ¾ of the rim diameter where the rim is equal to or greater than the height of the bowl. (I

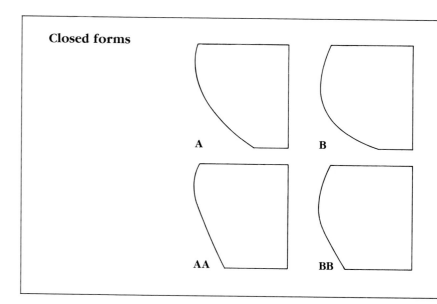

Closed forms

A   B

AA   BB

Squashed, closed forms can be intriguing, even secretive.

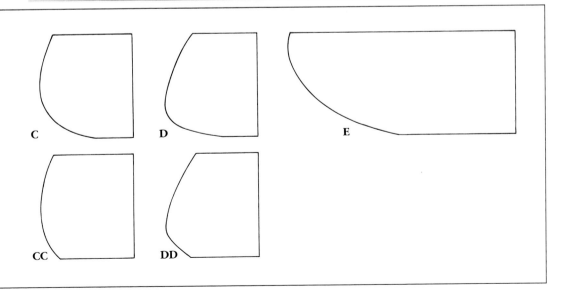

C

D

E

CC

DD

suspend this rule when the rim diameter is less than the height, and for the less practical vase forms.)

If you take a form similar to *B* and *C* on pp. 66-67 and continue the curve through the foot, you will wind up with a round base, as shown at left on the facing page. These slightly squashed spheres are some of my favorite forms. The curve flattens out as it approaches the rim and across the base, with the tightness kept below center. The result is incredibly sensual, almost erotic. The squashed sphere is important for two reasons. A perfect sphere will roll about, even with a lot of wood in the base. And spheres don't look good on a flat surface; their proper environment is space.

A foot placed beneath an enclosed form presents many of the same problems encountered with the open bowls. The curved feet in *A* and *C* at right on the facing page do not work as well as the more decorative, beaded feet in *B*, *D* and *E*. The bottom of the foot at *D* is too thin and needs a wider chamfer, as shown at *E*.

Queensland rosewood mahogany, 8-in. (200mm) diameter.

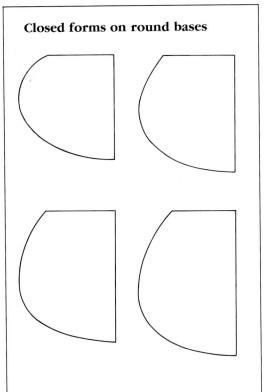

Closed forms on round bases

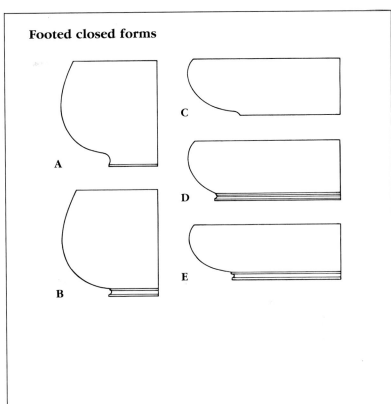

Footed closed forms

A

B

C

D

E

Combinations and angles Let's look at some of the ways in which the curves on the preceding pages might be combined. The eye will always be drawn to any point on a profile where there is a sudden change in direction. In the bowls below, a line is created where the foot meets the wall. This line may be harder or softer, but it must nevertheless be positioned with care, considering the guidelines for proportions. If horizontal lines are scattered arbitrarily up and down the profile, there will be little or no harmony in the form.

At the top of the facing page are four classical forms. At *A*, the foot is cut from the sweep of the curve. The point at which the profile changes direction and the bottom edge of the foot remain on the line of the curve. At *B*, the eye is jarred by the foot, which does not relate well to the upper curve. Also, the line defined by the junction of the foot and wall is too high, making the form slightly top-heavy.

Where concave shapes are combined, the balance is maintained by keeping the relevant reference points of the profile in a straight line, as shown at *C* and *D*. The top of the foot at *C* shouldn't be any higher, and is certainly not as restful as that at *D*, which is one-fifth the height of the whole.

In the first column of the lower drawing on the facing page, only *A* really works. Here the upper concave curve springs nicely away from the convex curve below. It contrasts well with *B*, where the points lie on a straight line but the junction of the concave and convex curves is too high, and with *C*, where the curves are reversed and the form is heavier. At *D* is a form that always seems to look top heavy. The problem lies first in the way the shallow curve relates to the foot, and then where the concave curve sweeps to the rim. The same curve on a wider foot, such as *DD*, looks better, but the form is still a trifle heavy. Of the chunkier forms, only *E* is unsatisfactory—the line that divides the upper and lower sections is too high. The profile at *H* is a better solution.

Convex and concave curves can be combined with interesting results. At left, Macassar ebony. At right, African blackwood. Both 5-in. (125mm) diameter.

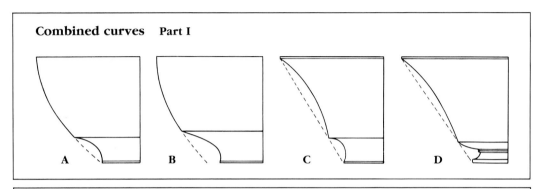

Combined curves   Part I

A   B   C   D

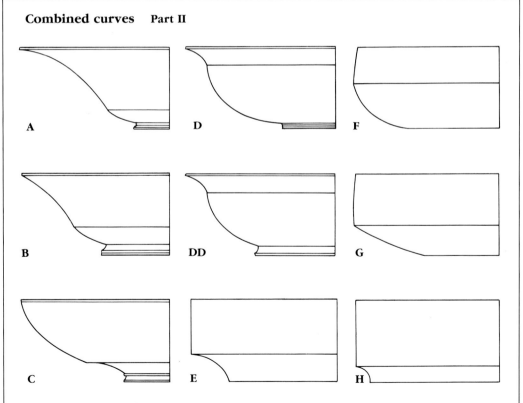

Combined curves   Part II

A   D   F

B   DD   G

C   E   H

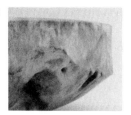

Subtle curves can have a visible impact, even in this jarrah-burl bowl.

In the bowl profile in the photo at left, the soft ogee reverses out to the bottom of the vertical to create a nice variation, enhanced by the gentle curve in the upper wall. The drawing on the facing page and the photo at the top of the facing page show how different curves—in the case of the photo, a convex curve and a concave curve—can be combined to create enclosed forms that are ideal for potpourri.

Internal form and rims Stunning grain and color can be combined with a subtle profile to create a wonderful-*looking* bowl. But if it's to *feel* as good as it looks you will have to pay as much attention to the internal form and the rim as you did to the exterior. The amount of wood you remove during hollowing, and the distribution of the wood that remains in the wall, will determine the physical weight and balance of the bowl. The shape of the rim affects first your visual perception of the bowl and then your sense of touch as you pick it up.

The internal space can be open or enclosed. In either case, the inside line of the wall does not have to parallel the outside line, but it should relate to it. The form you choose will depend largely on how the bowl will be used. In general, open forms are best for display or for food storage in which the contents will lie relatively undisturbed before being lifted or poured out. Enclosed forms are more secretive and containing, so I think of them for precious items, such as jewelry.

The sensations you experience in handling a bowl should confirm what your eye has programmed your brain to expect. Sad to say, this rarely happens. Sure, a really ugly bowl almost never feels good, but a surprising number of handsome bowls don't feel very good either. Too many turners strive for uniform thickness (or, more aptly, thinness), which usually results in boring bowls, lacking both subtlety and drama. Thin, uniform walls might sell well, and they are rarely as delicate or impractical as they appear. But ever since I discovered that I could turn a thin wall, I have found it more rewarding to tackle the chunkier forms and explore the subtleties of mass.

There are two major and related problems to overcome during hollowing. First, it is very difficult to achieve a smooth internal curve without using your eye—instead, you must rely upon your hand to feel the curve. And it is even more difficult to position that curve so that it complements the outer profile. I usually develop the internal curve from both ends. I cut the upper wall down from the rim, having first drilled a depth hole to establish the bottom.

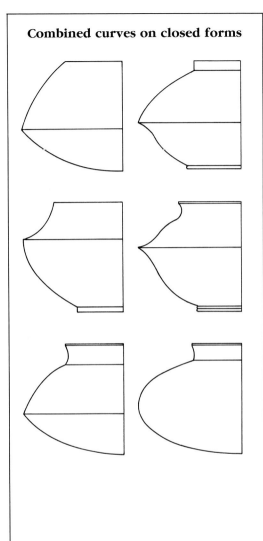

Combined curves on closed forms

On a truly successful bowl, the inner curve must relate well to the outside profile. Grass tree, 12-in. (305mm) and 10-in. (255mm) diameters.

Once the form is roughly hollowed, I work the bottom curve up to meet the rim curve. Here the potters may be right: If you get each end of your curve started right, the middle section will almost take care of itself. This takes practice, however, and even then, only a few turners get it absolutely right more than 10% of the time.

The thickness of the wall dictates the overall balance of a bowl. If a bowl wall is too thick at the rim it will be top-heavy. Conversely, if too much wood is left in the bottom, the bowl can feel as though ballast has been let into its base for extra stability. There is no universal equation for a well-balanced bowl. The characteristics vary somewhat with the form: The weight can be evenly distributed in the wall of a classic salad bowl, for example, because its broad base provides stability, whereas you expect extra weight in the foot of a fine-walled bowl.

Achieving the right relationship between the inside and outside profiles is at the heart of the bowl turner's art. I can offer no magic formula, but there can be little real progress without somehow exposing the wall profiles. A few bowls with amputated rims that expose the wall profile, such as the cut-sided bowls in Chapter 5, can be analyzed easily enough. But otherwise you will have to commit the terrible deed, which I'm sure my students must dread: You will have to cut your bowl in half.

This is a common practice among potters, who are fortunate to work with a reusable material. I'm sure it accounts, at least in part, for the large number of excellent ceramic bowls. I suspect that the comparable dearth of top-quality wooden bowls reflects the failure of turners to indulge in a similar exercise. I strongly recommend you slice in two any bowl that you know to be inferior—you will learn so much from the profile. What's more, the process will enforce a less precious approach to your craft.

At left are examples of what I consider to be the best and the worst in run-of-the-mill bowls. The inside one—9½-in.-(245mm) dia. English walnut—is one of the first large bowls I ever made back in 1970. (Note the contrast between the freshly sanded wood on the cross section and the darker, oxidized surface elsewhere—wood really *does* change color.) The lighter, 14-in.-(355mm) dia. ash bowl is one of my standard production bowls from around 1979.

The inside bowl displays several features common in beginners' bowls. To begin with, the diameter of the base was dictated by the 6-in.- (150mm) dia. faceplate that was used to attach it to the lathe. (The recess in the base located the center of the faceplate.) The exterior profile is rather innocuous, although it would have looked

All is revealed in the cut profiles of these archetypal good (outside) and bad (inside) salad bowls.

much better had it met the base at a definite angle instead of at a sloppy radius, and if the curve had swept in more to create a narrower base. But this bowl really pales when we consider its inner profile—the epitome of everything I hope now to avoid. The shallow V across the bottom meets the wall much too abruptly, leaving too much wood on the rim of the base. Farther up the wall, the curve flattens out again before arriving indecisively at the rim. This is a fine example of a curve that doesn't flow and it contrasts well with the larger bowl.

On the ash-bowl profile, the flat external curve rises decisively away from the base, tightening gradually toward the rim. The internal curve sweeps around smoothly, relating to—but not copying—the outside profile. There are no dips or bumps to mar its flow. The rim makes a definite statement, and the way in which the inner lip is cut back slightly towards the profile creates a shadow within that emphasizes the form.

These bowls contrast even more when handled—the ash bowl is much better balanced. The wall is thinner below the rim, which takes away much of the weight in the upper part of the bowl and leaves a nice balance between the masses of the rim and base. The slight dovetail shape of the cut-back rim also makes the bowl easy to lift using one hand. The rim fits snugly between fingers and thumb, inspiring confidence. The external sweep of the profile makes it easy to lift using two hands since there is enough room to get your fingers beneath the bulk of the bowl. The walnut bowl fails badly by comparison. The sides are too steep to allow the bowl to be lifted easily with two hands. And if you use just one hand, the thin tapering wall and rounded rim will tend to slip from your fingers and thumb if you don't hang on tight.

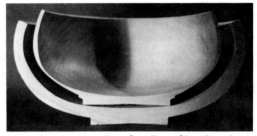

Two classic examples of wall profiles that don't quite make it.

At right are two other bowls that have a less-than-satisfactory cross section. Both have good exterior profiles and would have had rounded bases, but I aborted them before turning away the foot—the inside bowl because of wall thinness, the outside one because the wood is totally lackluster. The inner curve of the lower bowl descends from the rim in just the right direction, with the wall profile narrowing slightly. The sweep across the base is just right, but the two internal curves don't flow together. The line takes a short-cut across the fullness of the curve, leaving the wall over-thick about one-third of the distance from the bottom. This leaves an excess of wood halfway up the wall, and the form is weighted unevenly towards the base.

On the upper cross section, I should have left more wood in the rim before returning toward the base. Even though I got the line wrong at the outset, I could have salvaged the bowl by gradually increasing the wall thickness and fairing it into the curve that sweeps across the bottom.

Part of the problem here was that I drilled the initial depth hole a bit too deep. Although I got the sweep across the base just right, it's in the wrong place for the wall thickness that I had intended. When I cut down from the rim I failed to bring the gouge around quickly and evenly enough. When I finally saw the light, it was coming through the wall, and the bowl was beyond redemption. Had I measured more accurately, I would have taken the upper section of the wall down to the same thickness as the lower portion, even though I am not fond of such delicacy in a functional 12-in. (305mm) bowl. Such thin bowls are impractical and tend to become mere demonstrations of technical expertise.

A small-footed form requires extra weight in the foot for stability. The bowl pictured at left on the top of the facing page has just enough mass in all the right places. The wall thickens gracefully as it approaches both rim and foot; the simple outer profile and the internal catenary curve are an elegant combination.

I tried to achieve the same balance in the deeper bowl at right on the top of the facing page, but missed. The outer profile flows nicely away from the foot, but I began the inside cut at the wrong angle and couldn't rescue it when the green wood warped. In trying to duplicate the outer profile, I pivoted the gouge forward too quickly and nearly went through the wall. The wall doesn't feel as bad as it looks in the photograph, but the bowl is a little top-heavy, despite the extra wood in the foot.

Rims The rim of a bowl is linked inextricably with both the inside and the outside walls. Rims deserve far more attention than they get. Too often the top of the wall is cursorily rounded over, or otherwise vaguely or sloppily executed. A good rim can ensnare the eye while encircling secretive depths, or create illusions of thickness and thinness, or look so sensual that the urge to fondle it becomes irresistible.

The infinite variety of turned rims can be divided into four general groups: flat, inclining inward, inclining outward and rolled-over. Each of these can be made thick or thin, as well as convex, concave or ogee-shaped. Non-turned rims can be waney-edged (often called free-form), carved or eccentric, which covers all the rest.

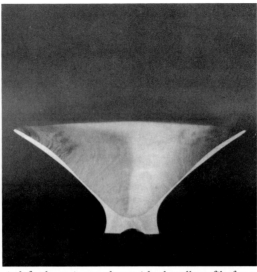

At left above is an almost ideal wall profile for a small bowl. The bowl above could have sold easily, but there was much more to be gained by cutting it in half and studying its shortcomings.

Rosewood mahogany, 11-in. (280mm) diameter. The grooves relieve an otherwise stark form as they frame the rim.

Jarrah, 12-in. (305mm) diameter.

Flat rims   A plain flat rim is rigid and boring, but may be eased by coves or beads. The edges of the rim at left are in the same horizontal plane, but the top of the rim has been dished for interest. The flat rim of the bowl at the bottom of p. 77 has been enlivened by shallow beads.

Inclining-inward rims   Below, the top two photos show the same rim from two different angles. In the low view you can see that the rim is slightly convex and that the wall has been cut back steeply inside it. This accents the inside of the rim with a shadow, which is clearly seen in the top view. The effect is a rim that encloses the bowl with a bright ring. The bottom two photos below show the effect of light on simple and complex curves. The convex rim at left is more sensual to hold, while the concave rim at right is much more interesting visually. The top photo on the facing page shows the dramatic effect that can be achieved with a large, sloping rim.

The ash bowl, top left and right, has a ⅝-in.- (15mm) thick wall and a good rim for a production salad bowl. The small cove on the rim of the jarrah-burl bowl at bottom left helps enclose the space and halts the long flow of the line from the base.

Inclining-outward rims   The jarrah-burl bowl at the center of the facing page required a strong rim to offset the rough exterior. The beads on the rim's inner edge mark the boundary between within and without, and the inside wall drops steeply to ensure definition between the two.

On the large bowl at the bottom of the facing page, the slope of the rim and the steep inside wall meet at an angle of about 75°, making it comfortable for the hand to hold.

The undercut inner rim and well-defined lip creates the shadow, while the curve of the outer rim catches the light to emphasize the two planes. Queensland rosewood mahogany, 14-in. (355mm) diameter.

Top: The beads at the inner edge of the rim lend structure to an inherently unruly outer form. Jarrah burl, 14-in. (355mm) diameter. Bottom: The rims on these jarrah bowls were designed to be fondled.

Various devices may be used to highlight the inside edge of a rim and reduce the harshness of a plain angle or a broad, unbroken line. Some of my favorites are the beads shown on the jarrah-burl bowl on the previous page, the cove shown immediately below, and the raised band shown at the bottom of the page. I left the unfinished surface from the chainsaw on top of the band to contrast with the smooth curve on either side. The band protrudes above the rim and encloses the inner space like a little wall. The underside of the wide rim at the top on the facing page is detailed with a bead to emphasize the transition between the rim and wall and to relieve the stark form, which is not of a highly figured wood.

Rolled-over rims I usually round over thin wall rims for safety as much as for tactile reasons: Sharp rims can cut and should always be softened. In the bowl at far right on the facing page, the rim is rounded to an arc. In the center photo on the facing page, the maker has flared and rounded this subtle rim, creating a hint of shadow on both inner and outer lips. I find a voluptuous rim, like the one in the bottom photo on the facing page, by far the best to handle. The inside meets the rim at an angle approaching 90°, but the curve rolls right over into the outside of the wall.

Top: A small cove softens the corner of the inner lip and adds interest, while defining the change of surfaces. Bottom: Its raised rim makes this bowl a good repository for keys and small change.

Top left: This type of detail tucked away out of sight or in shadow is a treat to discover. Queensland rosewood mahogany, 14-in. (355mm) diameter. Above: Rounded-over rims are inviting and, on thin-walled bowls, protect idle fingers from getting cut. English walnut, 6-in. (150mm) diameter. Center left: The rim on this bowl, made by Simon Raffan of Lillydale, Tasmania, flares gently on both sides. English alder, 10-in. (255mm) diameter. Bottom left: This rolled-over rim fits securely in the hand and is a pleasure to hold. Jarrah burl, 10-in. (255mm) diameter.

Carved rims The sequence below shows different views of the same bowl. Thanks to its carved rim, the bowl presents a different aspect from every angle.

The saddle shape of the bowl at the top of the facing page is cut to follow the line of the growth rings. This presents two completely different profiles. (The other one is shown on p. 53, on the left.)

Finally, a rim may be carved with dramatic effect. The rim of the bowl at bottom left on the facing page was carved by Alan Stirt, of Enosburg Falls, Vermont, to create a nice contrast against the smoothly polished surface. Likewise, the striations across the 2½-in.-(65mm) wide rim at far right contrast dramatically with the smooth interior. I achieved this effect by simply leaving the chain-saw marks on the finished rim.

The carved rim on this 6-in.- (150mm) dia. goldiewood bowl presents a different aspect from each side.

This bowl is visually balanced from all sides, the result of even growth rings and careful alignment on the lathe.

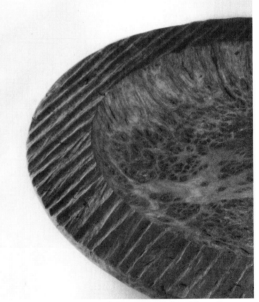

Left: Box-elder burl, 5-in. (125mm) diameter. Right: The chainsaw marks left on the wide rim of this jarrah-burl bowl are a dramatic contrast with the interior.

Waney-edged rims White sapwood will emphasize a waney edge, but it's important to maintain a good visual balance. I take great care to align the blanks for waney-edged bowls like the ones immediately below so the high and low points of the rim lie in their respective horizontal planes. If the valleys are different depths, a bowl tends to look fine from one side only. If the upper points are not in the same plane, the form seldom works. At the bottom of the page is a bowl that just missed. The idea was to have one wing sweeping upwards, but the form ended up looking off-balance.

The urge to retain the surface texture of a burl is almost irresistible. The overhead view at the top of the facing page shows how the coarse rim works to enclose the smooth interior. From the side we might imagine ourselves intruding on a volcanic landscape.

Top: The rims on waney-edged bowls must be carefully aligned to avoid appearing off-balance. Bottom: If the high points of the rim are not in the same plane, the form will look unbalanced.

The other-worldly, live-edge rim of a jarrah-burl bowl.

Bases It is amazing how many people will look first at the underside of a bowl and then, with barely a glance at the form, pronounce judgment on your skill (or lack thereof). To be fair, most of these souls are woodworkers, not the public. Evidence of a screw faceplate or a spigot chuck does not appall me, as it does so many other turners, although I prefer not to see felt disguising a rough surface. I look for a well-finished base, sanded to the same standard as the rest of the bowl. Screw holes can be disguised, or plugged simply and cleanly as shown below. Rabbets for expanding-collet chucks, seen in the bottom photo, can be detailed so that anyone unfamiliar with lathe equipment might not guess the purpose of the "decoration."

These days, I turn almost every base—whether it's to make a smooth, rounded bottom or a detailed foot, as on the facing page. But if I were still doing quantities of production salad bowls, I think I would stick to plugging the holes, which would keep the price about 20% lower. Beautifully turned bases never increased my sales.

Top: A simple plug makes a good finish to a bowl mounted on a single screw. Bottom: A groove helps disguise the utilitarian nature of this rabbet, which was used to fit an expanding-collet chuck.

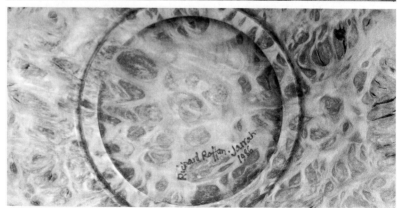

This bowl was almost finished when it was fitted in a jam-fit chuck, so the foot could be turned to complete the job.

Developing Profiles

Ialways follow the same basic steps when I make a bowl. I turn the outside profile first and then remount it for hollowing. Finally, I reverse the bowl again to finish the foot if this was not done during the first stage. I will chuck and re-chuck a piece of timber up to five times in the course of turning a bowl. The number of times depends on the size, the finish of the base, and whether the bowl is rough-turned or not. This process requires the use of several different chucks (or faceplates), and these are described later in this chapter (see pp. 100-101).

In this section, I will demonstrate the subtleties involved in developing and refining several of my favorite profiles. I generally use a pulled scrape cut for heavy roughing, and back cuts for finishing. These and other cutting techniques are described fully in *Turning Wood with Richard Raffan.*

So far, we have looked at bowls the right way up, even if much of the time (in the drawings) you have seen only half the bowl. It would be ridiculous, however, to remove a bowl from the lathe every time you want to see how the profile is developing, so you must get used to viewing the form on its side. I try to watch the top of the profile as I turn, and rarely stand back to assess the whole shape until the final stages. That's when I need to feel the curve and see how it relates to the base or foot.

In the sequence of photos on the facing page, I have mounted a 6-in. (150mm) by 14-in. (355mm) elm blank on a 6-in. (150mm) faceplate. The gap in the bed of this Woodfast 400 lathe normally

A	B	C	D	E

This sequence shows how a typical salad bowl may be developed on a relatively small lathe. Elm, 6 in. (150mm) by 14 in. (355mm).

accepts stock up to about 5¼ in. (130mm) thick by 17½-in. (450mm) dia., but by using the bandsaw to cut a wide chamfer around the blank, I can increase the bowl's depth. The disc was cut from a chainsawn slab, which accounts for its uneven thickness.

Roughing cuts are made from the base to the rim to true the blank as quickly as possible *(A)*. After the bulk of the rough corner has been removed, the profile is ready for development of the curve even though you can still see remnants of the bark.

The upper section has been cut back to remove the bark *(B)*, while the lower curve now sweeps in, reducing the base to about one-third the diameter of the rim. The tonal change indicates where the lower cut stopped and the upper one started. Beginning to finalize the curve *(C)*, I make a back cut using a deep-fluted ½-in. (13mm) gouge. I concentrate on moving with the tool and preventing any chatter as I proceed, barely looking at the line of the curve, which is already established. In photo *D* the curve is almost complete. Note that the tightest part of the curve is near the rim and that quite a bit of wood was removed to keep the curve flowing. The ridge will be removed with a final cut in from the face to keep the rim from splintering.

Now that the curve is refined, it's time to decide on the next fixing. I have two choices: either mount the base on a 4-in. (100mm) faceplate for hollowing, using two screws, or turn a foot for a three-jaw chuck. I choose the latter option, and turn a shallow foot for the chuck *(E)*. When the inside is finished I will reverse the bowl once more in a jam-fit chuck and turn the foot off.

A small, decorative, but functional bowl emerges through several possible profiles, dictated in part by the fractious nature of the burl. Jarrah burl, 6-in. (150mm) diameter.

At *A*, above, is a 6-in.- (150mm) dia. jarrah burl, mounted on a center-screw faceplate. (The rough disc was cut on the bandsaw.) Again working from the base to the rim, I use a shallow ½-in. (13mm) gouge to remove the corner's bulk *(B)*. (I seldom true the sides of a disc before starting the curve; I save time by truing the block and reducing the weight as I develop the curve, and forget about making a cylinder unless it's what I want). At *C* on the facing page the flat sections are gone, but I've left a cylinder below the rim to keep open my options for an enclosed form.

I decide, instead, to turn a footed bowl with an angled, open profile. At *D* on the facing page, I've marked the diameter of the spigot chuck on the bottom using a pair of dividers, and the foot begins to take shape. The foot is cut slightly oversize and the wall profile is developed. The final cut on the foot is left until the end, in case I have a catch that knocks the form off-center. Whenever possible, I leave finishing cuts until all roughing cuts are completed.

C

D

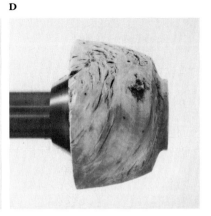

The upper curve is now developed, but the form looks heavy and a chunk is missing from the rim—a hazard with burls. To lift the form, I raise the line between the two curves, and angle the upper curve in towards the base, at *E* on the facing page. But the line seems too high, so I tighten the lower section of the upper curve further, which lowers the line. This develops a good profile *(F)*, which I detail with a small bead at the top of the foot.

The chunk missing from the rim forces me to cut the upper curve again. At *G* below, the upper curve is completed, but now I decide I don't really care for the angle, so it goes. In the final profile *(H)*, the diameter is reduced to 5½ in. (140mm) and all remnants of the angle have been eliminated. This is a typical example of the way in which wood—in this case, the disintegrating rim—can dictate the terms. At other times, difficult grain might have to be cut several times until you can get it clean. As you lose wood and the form changes, you will have to reassess the situation.

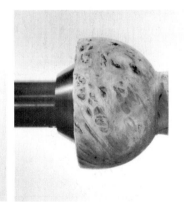

G

H

In photo *A* below, a 10¼-in.- (260mm) dia. spalted, liquid-amber blank is held to a large faceplate by two screws. (The two screws provide a better grip on the uneven top face than would a single, center-screw faceplate.) I use a Turnmaster 1-in. (25mm) gouge to make the initial cuts, removing the corner. I can use the gouge quite forcefully because the faceplate and the headstock of the lathe will absorb the pressure. If the form were reversed—with the much smaller base attached to the faceplate—I couldn't risk a fraction of the pressure unless massive screws secured the wood.

I always begin truing a bowl blank by getting rid of any bark, holes or other undesirable features. In *B,* most of the bark is turned

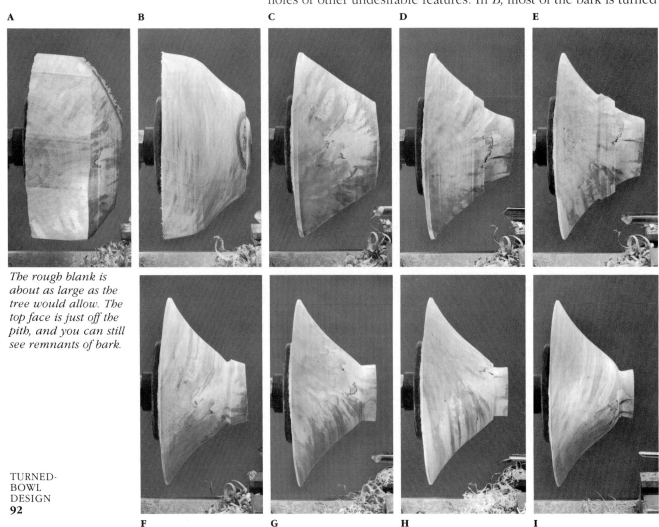

A B C D E

The rough blank is about as large as the tree would allow. The top face is just off the pith, and you can still see remnants of bark.

F G H I

away, and I can begin to consider the profile. This form could yield a full, convex curve on a narrow foot, but I decide instead to try for an outflowing concave shape, possibly on a foot.

My first step is to use a deep-fluted ½-in. (13mm) gouge to straighten up the side *(C)*. Although this is a long way from the shape I want, I try to cut the spalted wood as cleanly as possible, taking a close look at the surface for any defects. If I encounter any cutting problems at this stage, I'll have plenty of time to try different cuts or tools, so that I'll be ready to make a clean finished cut when the time comes.

Using a ⅜-in. (10mm) deep-fluted gouge, I develop the curve from the base *(D)*, trying to impart some upward thrust to the line. The stepped profile indicates where earlier cuts ended. This excess material gives me the option of cutting a tight curve up from the foot, and perhaps flattening it out towards the rim. Notice that the base still isn't trued; I prefer to keep the maximum amount of wood in the foot until I've determined its final diameter.

With a concave profile like this, I like to develop the curve from the rim. Holding the tools horizontally as I do, it is much easier to watch the line develop by cutting down from the rim rather than up from the base. You also have fewer leverage problems because you can keep the fulcrum nearer the point of cut, and if you move the gouge slowly and evenly you should have little trouble getting a clean cut.

Spalted liquid amber, 10¼-in. (260mm) diameter.

At *E,* I used two heavy roughing cuts to develop the form quickly, and the end grain has picked up a bit. Still cutting down from the rim, I fair the upper and lower curves together *(F)*, then pivot the tool forward at the end of the cut to create an ogee. I am mainly concerned with getting the curve right on the primary mass, while maintaining enough mass in the foot. By concentrating on the upper form, there is always the risk of reducing the diameter of the foot too much.

I use a ¼-in. (6mm) shallow gouge to cut the foot and detail the beads *(G)*. The curve looks pretty good, but the base is a little too wide and the foot a bit too stubby. In photo *H,* I narrow the foot to fit a spigot chuck, then ease the bottom of the curve into the top of the foot. In *I,* the foot is gently tapered, which leads the eye up to the primary mass. The junction between them is detailed with a coved bead to smooth the transition. At this point the foot can be sanded and finished, ready for the spigot chuck, which will hold it for hollowing. In the photo at right, the form split badly within half an hour, before I could hollow it—win a few, lose a few.

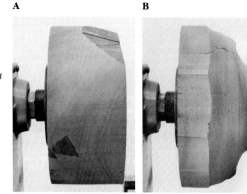

In this sequence, three good profiles emerge after a less-than-promising start. Note that a bad split is not a disaster if you proceed in the right manner. Rosewood mahogany, 11-in. (280mm) diameter.

In photo *A* above is an 11-in.- (280mm) dia. rosewood-mahogany blank, mounted on a faceplate. A large split reveals itself when the bulk of the corner is removed *(B)*. The blank is radically reduced at *C* to get rid of the split. In this situation, I eliminate any defects, while retaining as much usable material as possible. With the upper part of the split turned off *(D)*, I know what I have to play with and can begin to think seriously about the form. But first I block out the basic shape.

I establish the approximate diameter of the base *(E)*, thinking in terms of a simple, outflowing curve from base to rim. The concave profile develops quickly *(F)*, and it is easier to judge the proportions. I try to take these cuts in one pass from the base to the rim, using a ½-in. (13mm) deep-fluted gouge with a heavy backcut. Because it is difficult to see the profile develop from this position, I concentrate on moving smoothly through the curve and on sensing it develop. A final light cut with the same tool leaves a smooth flowing line and a good profile for a fruit bowl *(G)*. The wide base is stable enough, but doesn't make the form appear too heavy.

H   I   J

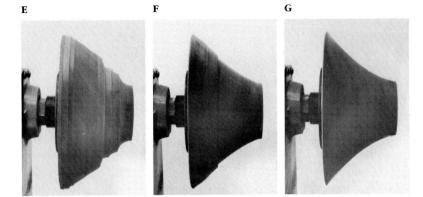

I could easily stop here, but decide to add a foot by cutting in at the base, as shown in photo *H* at the bottom of the facing page. I use a ½-in. (13mm) shallow gouge in a scraping cut, and the form lightens immediately as the primary mass is raised on the pedestal. A few more quick roughing cuts narrow the base slightly, and give a bit of extra lift. I mark the base for a spigot chuck now, then refine the curve and raise the top of the foot a bit with a finish cut *(I)*. But the curve of the foot flattens out at the top and needs attention. In *J*, I narrow the base slightly and raise the height of the foot a little more to repair the curve.

This is another good point to stop, but watch how the form can be adapted further. I curve the lower wall around to meet the top of the foot, and cut the foot to a taper, as in photo *K.* This develops an extra ring of material which can be turned into a bead at the top of the foot *(L)*. But this is a bit intrusive, so I cut a cove into the top of the bead, which makes a nice transition between the foot and the primary mass of the bowl. The finished bowl, shown in *M,* has warped slightly, and is typical of many of my more decorative bowls.

K   L   M

A　　　　**B**　　　　**C**　　　　**D**

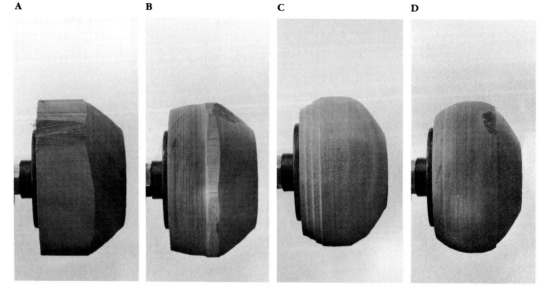

A rounded, enclosed form develops and beads are added for decoration. Rosewood mahogany, 9-in. (230mm) diameter.

To turn an enclosed bowl in the sequence at the top of these two pages, I start with a cylindrical, 9-in.- (230mm) dia. rosewood-mahogany blank, mounted on a faceplate. As usual, I begin by turning away the bottom corner of the blank *(A)*, but I removed more wood towards the base than up the side. Being careful to leave plenty of material for the fullness of the curve, I begin to develop the upper slope to the rim *(B)*. In *C*, I remove a lot of wood quickly in a series of stepped, scraping cuts from the rim, using a ½-in. (13mm) shallow gouge. The curve starts to take shape, but it looks a bit slumped. I reduce the lower part of the profile *(D)*, which will push the curve up the wall. This line would be just about right for a flat base, but because I plan to round the base, I need to create a small foot for the three-jaw chuck to hold the bowl for hollowing. I turn the foot *(E)*, then, still using the ½-in. shallow gouge, I continue the lower curve as far as I can without moving the tool rest.

Cutting back from the rim, I stop the cut short of joining the upper and lower curves. This leaves a ring proud of the surface, as shown in photo *F*, which I decide to turn into beads. The curve is cut cleanly so that it flows smoothly beneath the roughed bead. When the curve is complete, the beads are cut using a ¼-in. (6mm) gouge *(G)*. The profile is now ready to be sanded and re-mounted in the chuck for hollowing. The shallow foot has been turned off the bottom of the finished bowl, which is pictured in photo *H*.

E   F   G   H

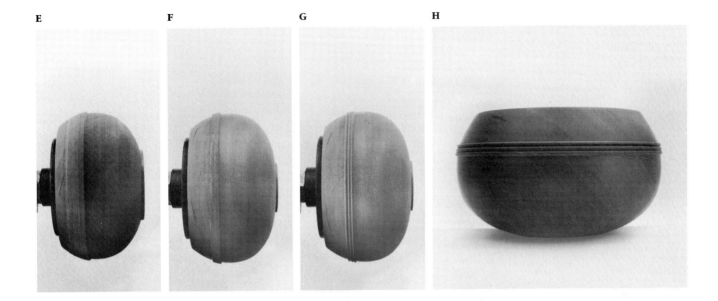

The safest way to turn the free-form jarrah burl shown in photo *A* below is between centers. The material is too fractious for screws and the eccentricity of the blank generates vibration until it is trued. In *B*, the blank is trued and ready for realignment. I want the two highest points of what will be the rim to be on the same horizontal plane and the two lowest points on another. The pencil lines show the position of the high points, and act as a guide while I pivot the blank around the spur drive. (A two-spur drive works best for this technique.) Once the high points are aligned, I do the same for the low points and turn a foot for the three-jaw chuck, which will hold the form for hollowing.

A single cut from the base to the rim refines the curve, as shown in *C*. The form is a bit pointy near the base, though, and the bottom curve is a little flat. So I start to cut down into the base, rolling a ½-in. (13mm) shallow gouge to define a corner at the top of the foot. The height of the bowl is reduced in *D*, as a secondary foot develops.

A typically unpromising-looking burl is mounted between centers. The cut facets are soon reduced to a good, full form, which may be developed into several different profiles. Jarrah burl, 9-in. (230mm) diameter.

A

B

C

D

In *E*, the first foot is turned away as much as possible, leaving just enough wood to support the tail center. This process is repeated, cutting down the slope from the rim to the base for the best possible view of the developing curve. Nearing completion, in *F*, the form is a lot squatter than the original blank and the upper curve turns in slightly at the rim. This is partly so the bowl will be more tactile, but also to make it fit in a jam-fit chuck, which I will use to hold the blank while the base is turned off. The finished bowl is pictured in *G*.

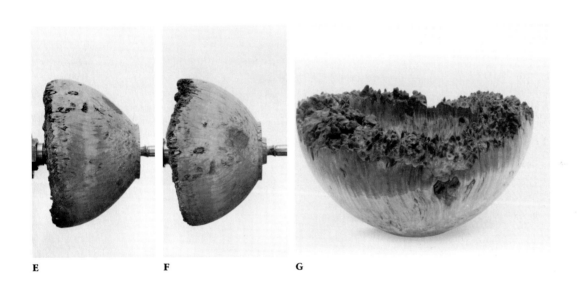

E   F   G

Notes on fixings There are many ways of securing a blank to the lathe. I could hold the wood by the base and turn the whole bowl in one go without changing the fixing, but I never do. I prefer to begin by holding the blank by the face that will be the top of the bowl. This allows me to work the outside profile from any direction. If some flaw emerges as the form develops, such as a bit of bark or a hole behind a knot, I can do something about it. It's better to discover these things at an early stage, rather than in the throes of final hollowing. Also, in the later stages of developing a profile, I often turn the base to improve the overall proportions. If a bowl is held by the base, there is no easy way to narrow the foot or reduce the height of the bowl without altering the upper wall.

The minor inconvenience of re-chucking the form for hollowing is totally eclipsed by being able to maintain your design options for as long as possible. Many of the newer chucks on the market enable you to grip a finished surface, and these days practically all of my small bowls are held for hollowing in one of my many spigot chucks.

The chart on the facing page indicates the options presented at each stage and the requirements for the next. The idea is to get to the final fixing as quickly as possible, while maintaining the freedom to adjust the design as work proceeds.

The choice of the first fixing depends on the quality of the top face. If it is smooth, I use a center-screw faceplate to hold all bowls up to 12 in. (305mm) by 4 in. (100mm), and a standard, multi-screw faceplate for larger or unbalanced blanks. But for the latter, I prefer a more secure fixing between centers, as shown in the photo sequence on pp. 98-99.

I never sand the profile during the first stage, in case the bowl is remounted off-center, which is often the case. But I do complete any area that I won't be able to get at later, such as the base.

To prepare a finished base for its final fixing on a standard faceplate, I drill two screw holes, as shown in the photo at left. These are marked and drilled before the base is sanded and polished, and will enable you to re-chuck the bowl accurately. If the wood is dry, as in the bowl in the photo, the screw holes should be aligned across the grain, which reduces the risk of splitting. (In wet wood, faceplate screws are placed along the grain—see pp. 104-105.)

Expanding-collet or spigot chucks are an excellent final fixing. If the bowl is slightly off-center, you can usually tap it lightly to get it running true in the chuck. If this doesn't work, you will have to turn it true. This means that any turned decoration within the base will not be centered perfectly, but you're probably the only one who will notice.

With screw holes drilled, the base can be sanded and oiled before mounting on a faceplate for hollowing. On dry wood, the screws are placed across the grain, which reduces the risk of splitting.

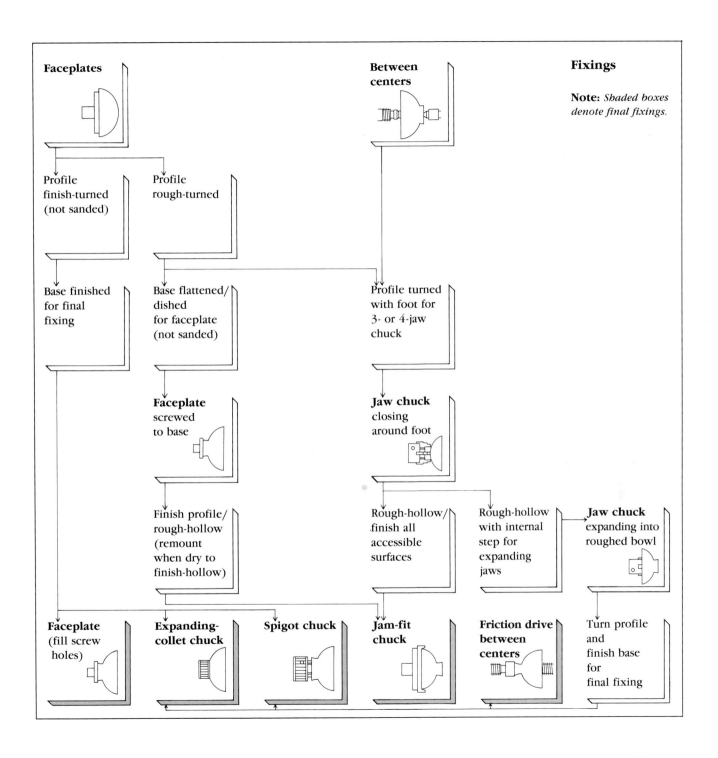

Faceplates

Between centers

Fixings

Note: *Shaded boxes denote final fixings.*

Profile finish-turned (not sanded)

Profile rough-turned

Base finished for final fixing

Base flattened/ dished for faceplate (not sanded)

Profile turned with foot for 3- or 4-jaw chuck

Faceplate screwed to base

Jaw chuck closing around foot

Finish profile/ rough-hollow (remount when dry to finish-hollow)

Rough-hollow/ finish all accessible surfaces

Rough-hollow with internal step for expanding jaws

Jaw chuck expanding into roughed bowl

Faceplate (fill screw holes)

Expanding-collet chuck

Spigot chuck

Jam-fit chuck

Friction drive between centers

Turn profile and finish base for final fixing

If your spigot chuck won't cope with the weight or uneven balance of your partially turned bowl, use the three-jaw chuck first, as shown below. In this case, the foot required by the chuck is too large for the form. So, after hollowing *(A)*, I reverse the bowl on the jaw chuck *(B)*, and turn a groove in the base to accept the flange of the spigot chuck *(C)*. Then I transfer the bowl to this for finishing *(D)*.

Using a spigot chuck, you can turn just about any shape you want for the foot, provided you can turn a groove somewhere on the foot that will fit the chuck. The bowl in the photo at the top of the facing page was gripped around the small bead at the top of the foot. In a variation of this, shown in the drawing on the facing page, I turn a shallow shoulder proud of the base for the spigot chuck to grip. This shoulder (shown in cross section in the drawing) is sanded off to complete the bowl. The base within the shoulder is recessed below the foot, so the bowl will rest on a concave base after the shoulder has been removed. This technique allows for a lot of

A three-jaw chuck may be used for rough-hollowing a form that is too heavy to be held in a spigot chuck, A. *After the bowl is hollowed, it may be reversed on the three-jaw chuck,* B. *The outside profile is then refined and a groove turned in the foot for the spigot chuck,* C *and* D, *which is the final fixing.*

A

B

C

D

Only a shallow, ⅟₃₂-in.- (1mm) deep groove was required to grip this bowl in a spigot chuck. The form was meant to resemble a bent plank perched on a plinth.

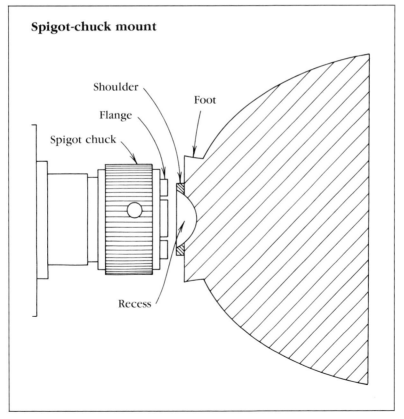

Spigot-chuck mount

Shoulder

Flange

Foot

Spigot chuck

Recess

freedom. I especially like to use it with green-turned bowls, where any decoration turned in the underside of the base will become oval—another nice touch.

The options that run down the center of the chart on p. 101 are used mainly for rough-turned bowls. Everything small enough for the three-jaw chuck is turned with a foot. This is mainly for speed and to eliminate the tiresome messing around with screws in faceplates. Large or eccentric bowls are held more securely on a faceplate for hollowing. (The screw holes can be turned off or filled later.) If you are roughing-out, remember that it is preferable to use two screws. But on wet wood, these should be aligned along the grain, as shown in the left-hand drawing on the facing page. If the holes are placed across the grain, they will move together as the wood dries, and you won't be able to relocate your screws in the same holes when it comes time to finish-turn the form. By locating these screws near the edge of the foot, as shown in the right-hand drawing, you will not sacrifice too much wood in the base. This foot can be turned off later, but you'll have to take care that the line of the wall profile is accurately projected through the foot to get the line you want around the base.

The option of mounting blanks between centers offers a quick and excellent technique for roughing-out bowls when you don't need to get at the base except to true it up. It's also very safe, provided the tail center is kept tight. You can pivot a blank around the drive to realign the grain patterns, as shown in the photo.

A waney-edged, or free-form, bowl is also best mounted between centers, so that you can get the rim exactly where you want it. (See the photos on pp. 98-99.) There is no other way to realign the partially completed form on the lathe while developing the profile.

The lower right corner of the chart on p. 101 looks complicated, but it offers several valuable options. The three- and four-jaw chucks are wonderfully flexible and enable work to proceed in a fast and loose manner. When you rough-turn a profile and foot you need not be too accurate. Just make sure the foot is small enough to fit the chuck, and that the base of the foot is flat, or slightly concave, so it fits true in the jaws. It's easy to grip the distorted foot of a roughed-out bowl, and you can expand the jaws to grip the inside. When you're rough-hollowing a bowl, leave a step near the top of the inside curve for the jaws of the chuck to butt against when you remount it for finishing, as shown in the photo on p. 33. (You can realign the bowl at this stage by tilting it over the jaws. If this looks unsafe, bring in the tail center for support, but make sure it is dead-center before switching on the power, or your bowl might fly.)

Among the final fixings I enjoy the least are the jam-fit chucks, or carriers, and the friction-drives between centers. With the former, the bowl always threatens to fly out of the chuck and shatter at the last moment, which is dangerous as well as irritating. With the latter, it can be hard to get the bowl running true, and there is always the risk of friction marks if the grip is not secure. More and more, I prefer the jaw and spigot chucks for their safety and flexibility.

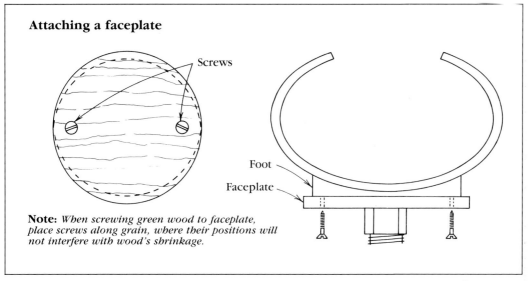

Attaching a faceplate

Screws

Foot

Faceplate

Note: *When screwing green wood to faceplate, place screws along grain, where their positions will not interfere with wood's shrinkage.*

The grain of a small, eccentric blank is most easily aligned between centers by pivoting the blank around the two-spur drive.

Cut sides Until now, we've devoted all our attention to voluptuous forms—elegant, outward-flowing concave curves, secretive, round containers, etc. But turned bowls do not have to be round. You can mix round and angular forms with dramatic effect, as shown at left. You can turn a hollow within a faceted form, such as the nine- and seven-sided bowls below. The vertical sides of the bowl on the left are flat and rectangular. By contrast, the sides of the bowl on the right are gently curved and its underside is convex, creating the scalloped lower edge of the facet. Rather than sand the facets smooth, I prefer to leave the bandsawn striations, which contrast nicely with the otherwise polished surfaces.

This claret-ash bowl, made by Frank Willcock of Benalla, Victoria, Australia, combines a round form with a cut-sided pedestal.

Cutting flat facets is easy using a bandsaw or tablesaw, but establishing where to cut and overcoming the inherent danger of corners and edges as you turn can create some problems. If you cut the sides before you mount the blank on the lathe, there are two points to consider. First, you must center the blank accurately on the lathe—if it is not absolutely true, the sides will not be equidistant from the inner lip of the rim. Second, because the corners protrude, crisp angles are difficult to maintain—they splinter easily during turning, and are rounded quickly during sanding. And the angular corners are dangerous.

Both problems are overcome if you cut the sides after the turned surfaces are completed. Or you can laminate temporary, protective blocks to the cut sides, as shown at top right on the facing page, so

Curved, cut sides in combination with a convex lower curve, at far right, create more subtle facets than the straight-sided form at right.

that the blank is turned within the safety of a disc. I don't always bother to laminate blocks to the end grain, which leaves short, flat areas on the rim of the disc, but these are no more hazardous than any rough-cut blank. The cut sides of the bowls at bottom right were prepared in this manner. Their angular shape was inspired by Japanese cut-sided ceramic dishes.

Once the sides are cut, they are usually smoothed. You can use a hand plane, but I prefer a disc or belt sander. A tilting sander table makes it easy to cut angles, although with a bit of fiddling, you can achieve the same results using wedges on a flat table, or cutting them freehand. The curve of the side varies with the angle presented to the sander and the top surface of the rim. From above, the concave rims of the bowls in the photo below make the edges look curved, although they are actually flat in one plane.

Even if you plan to cut the sides after the bowl is turned (as I usually do), it's easier to lay them out first on the rough-turned form. Before the bowl is hollowed, you must true its top face and mark the center with a sharp point. The face must be flat and reasonably smooth, even coarse-sanded, to produce a surface suitable for drawing. It is easier to do the drawing on a horizontal surface, so take the bowl off the lathe—preferably keeping it in the chuck so it remains centered. If this is unstable, make a cradle to support both bowl and chuck. A scribed line will survive all but the heaviest sanding, so it is preferable to a pencil line for marking the faces

Rectangular blanks of Macassar ebony are laminated with protective softwood, top, so that the cut sides will be contained within a disc for safe turning. The bowls above were turned from similar blanks. The softwood is cut off after the bowl is turned, and the sides are sanded smooth.

The straight cut sides on these ebony bowls appear from the top to be curved—a result of the concave shape of the wide rim.

that will be cut. Use dividers to mark arcs and a scribing knife or awl for straight lines.

To make a template for cut-sided bowls like the one shown in the photo at the top of the facing page, adhere an enlarged photocopy of one of the figures below (or construct one of your own) to a disc of clear plastic. Drill a small hole at center and at regular intervals along the radial lines, which you can locate by scribing circles of different diameters. Then remove your pattern. You can use this template on forms of different sizes simply by using different holes. (It is easier to locate the correct set of holes if the outline of each concentric circumference is marked on the template.)

Before marking the radial lines (which connect each point along the rim with the center) on the wood, you must locate the template on the bowl face with pins, inserted through at least two holes in the template, as shown in the photo at the top of the facing page. (I use small nails the same diameter as the holes to prevent any movement in the template.) Start with a nail in the center hole to center the template.

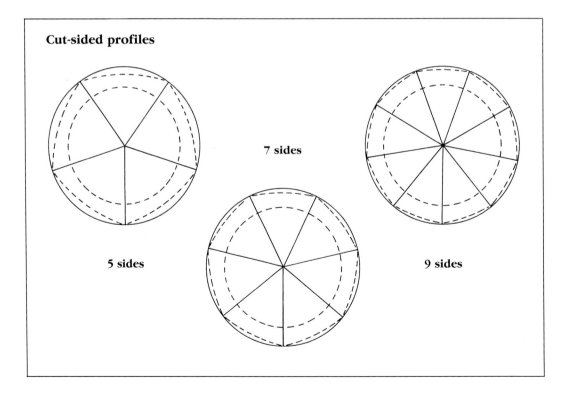

Cut-sided profiles

5 sides

7 sides

9 sides

If you are working on a partially turned bowl, locate the center nail in the pin prick at center and tap it into the wood. The template should rotate on the nail, enabling you to align the facets exactly to take into account grain orientation or any defects in the wood before inserting the second nail. Once the template is secured, ensure that it lies flat against the wood at the points you mark. The farther you mark the wood from center along each radial line, the more likely you are to absorb small errors in the template. Then remove the template and draw straight lines from the center through the radial points to the rim. These lines must be transferred down the sides, as shown at left below, to serve as a guide for cutting the facets after the inside and rim have been turned away.

Straight facets are marked out by joining the points where each radial line cuts the rim. If the facets are to be curved, I scribe the lines using a compass, a template or an engineer's curve. If you have no large compass or dividers with which to scribe a line, you can use a length of dowel with a nail at each end, as shown at right below. In the photo, the center of the arc is at the bottom. (Note that I have employed a square cardboard box as a cradle for the bowl blank, which is still mounted on its chuck.) To mark concave facets, I use the same reference points and a series of engineer's curves or templates.

Using these simple tools you can make all kinds of geometric shapes. The figures on the facing page offer a few suggestions and, hopefully, will resurrect any long-lost geometry from your school days. All that stuff you always knew would be useful...someday!

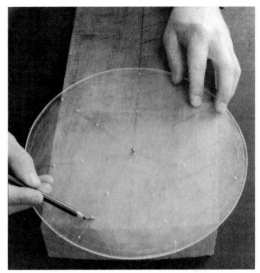

Using a template to mark a seven-sided bowl blank. Note the two pins that fix the template in position.

Far left: The radial lines marking the corners of each facet are extended down the sides to provide a guide after the face of the bowl has been turned. Left: You can mark the curved facets with a makeshift compass.

Profile templates The profiles on pp. 112-117 are not there just to look at. I suggest you select a few to copy, and that you make a template to help you get the curve right. Don't let the notion of copying bother you—it's an excellent way to learn about form and to develop your eye. In the workshop where I began to turn, I was given templates to use for all the standard bowls. When I started working on my own, I continued to use templates for all my basic profiles for about a year. As my eye improved, I needed the templates less and less. I was making large production runs of sugar bowls and salad sets—including one large and six or eight small bowls—and the practice they provided soon rendered the templates obsolete.

The templates will be most useful to beginners, although a number of professional turners might want to give them a whirl, too—especially when trying a new form. A good exercise is to make sets of 6-in.- (150mm) dia. bowls. You aren't likely to get complete sets in the beginning, but the effort will almost certainly yield a number of saleable individual pieces. It is ironic that by marketing these "failures" to reluctant craft shops in the early years of my career, I created the demand for the limited-production, "one-off" bowls that I now enjoy. The seeds of later success were sown by earlier ineptitude.

These profiles are meant to provide overall line and proportion. Detailing is up to you. If you want to include a bead or two, work out where it should go and cut it into the template. Feet have purposely been left undefined to allow you to adapt them to your own style. If your second fixing is a three-jaw chuck (typically used for rough-turning), you must add a foot or step so there will be a rim to grip. You should by no means limit yourself to the shapes on these pages—there are many others throughout this book and in books and magazines around the world. These are forms on which to build, and from which you can develop.

Make your templates from hardboard or thin plywood, or even metal or plastic if you plan to use them for production. The best method is to trace the outline on thin paper, and then adhere this to the template material for cutting. (And don't forget that the template should retain the negative shape of the profile.)

Once the blank is mounted on the lathe, true it to the overall dimensions of the bowl. First establish its thickness (which will be the height of the bowl), making sure to keep the bottom face flat. If it is concave you will lose thickness when you cut back to define the base.

Next, establish the diameter of the bowl and mark this on the base or top face. It is probably better to allow some extra room for your first attempts—perhaps ⅛ in. (3mm) in overall diameter. You can always reduce the curve to the right diameter once it fits the template. Develop regular methods of work. Your forms will be easier to duplicate if you go through the same process each time, and in this way your personal style will develop.

Finally, mark the diameter of the base or foot. With all these measurements set, you can begin turning away the waste to develop your shape. Templates are tedious to use because you need to stop to check so often, but their long-term benefits make it all worthwhile. In the heat of comparing your work to the template, don't forget to *touch* and *feel* the developing form. The quality of a curve is tactile as much as it is visual, and, as your eye develops, so too will your sense of touch.

Using a template

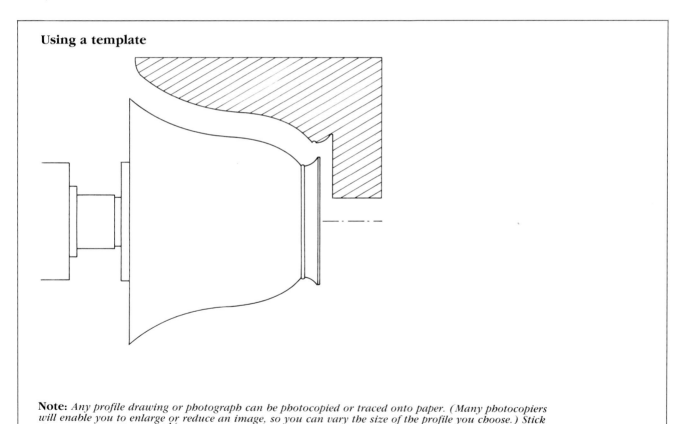

Note: *Any profile drawing or photograph can be photocopied or traced onto paper. (Many photocopiers will enable you to enlarge or reduce an image, so you can vary the size of the profile you choose.) Stick the copy to a stiff sheet of ⅛-in. (3mm) Masonite, wood or plastic, and then cut along the line of the profile. Use the negative portion as the template. Always stop the lathe before holding the template to the developing profile of your bowl.*

Template drawings

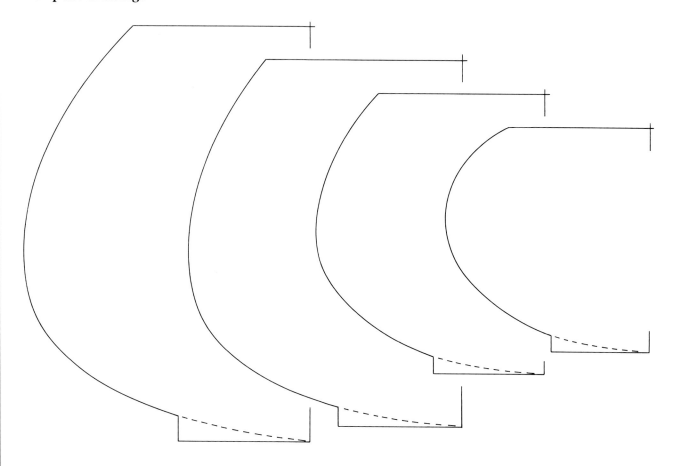

Note: *To better assess the half-profiles on the next six pages, simply hold a mirror on the centerline at a right angle to the page. The reflection will show the full form of the curve.*

The dotted line in the bowls on this page represents the final curve of the bottom profile. The foot, which is required to chuck the bowl for hollowing, is later removed.

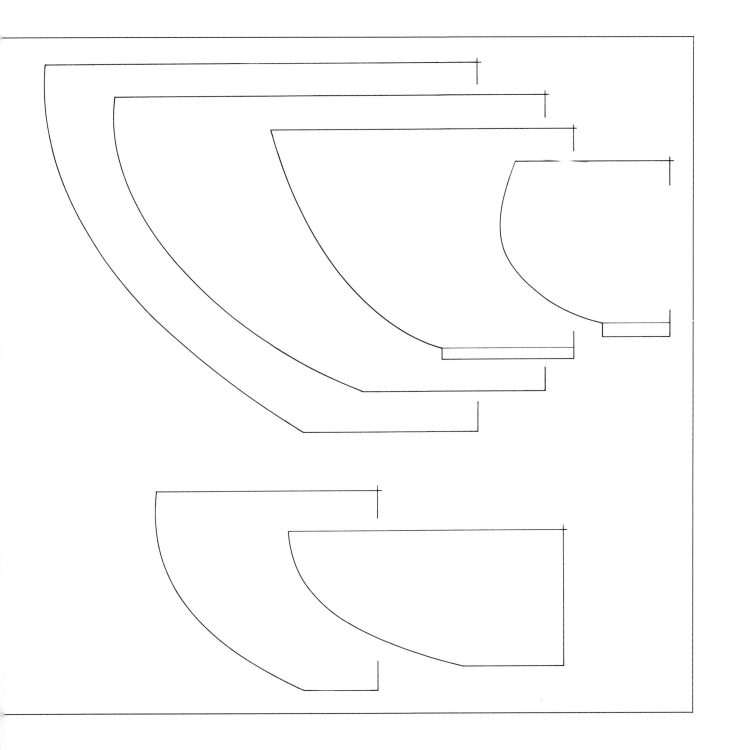

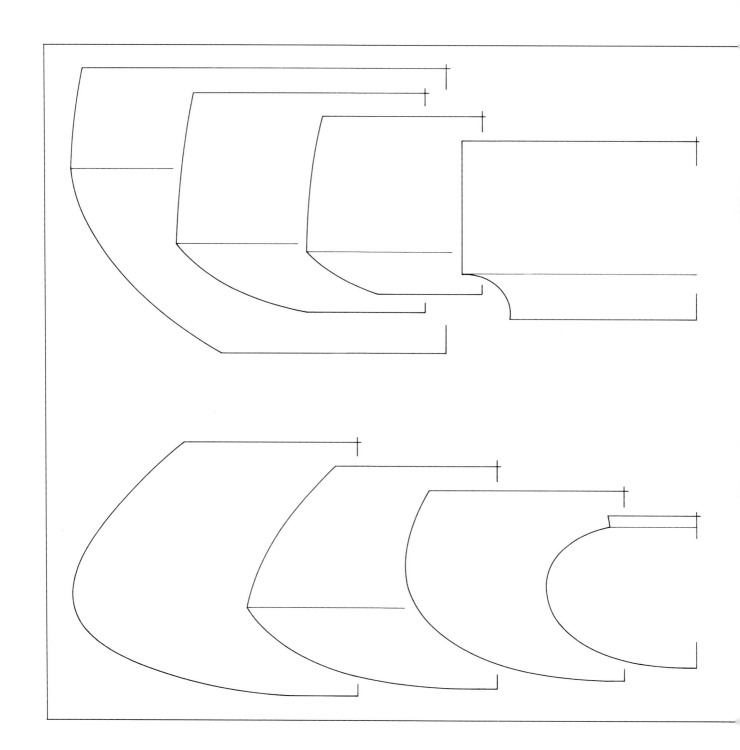

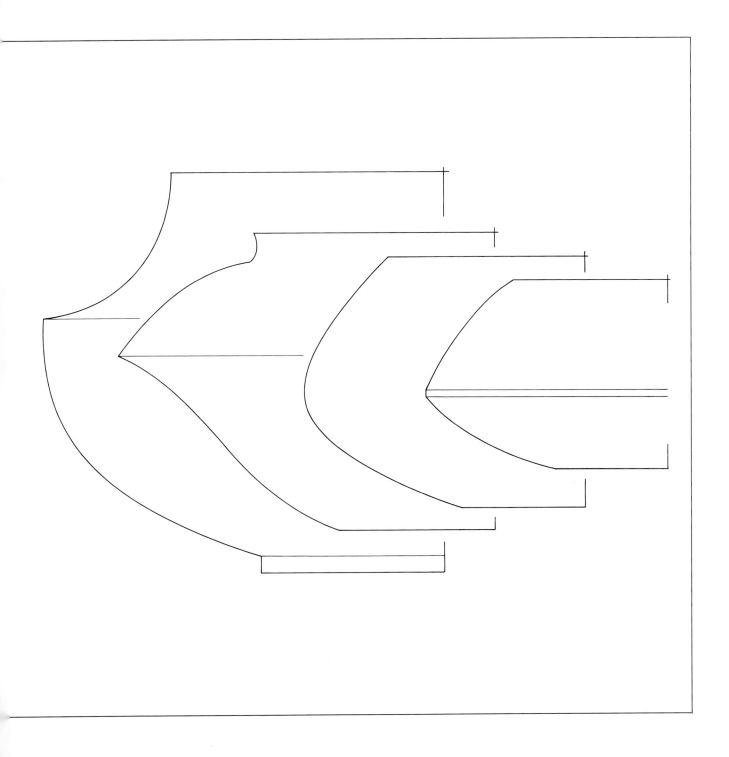

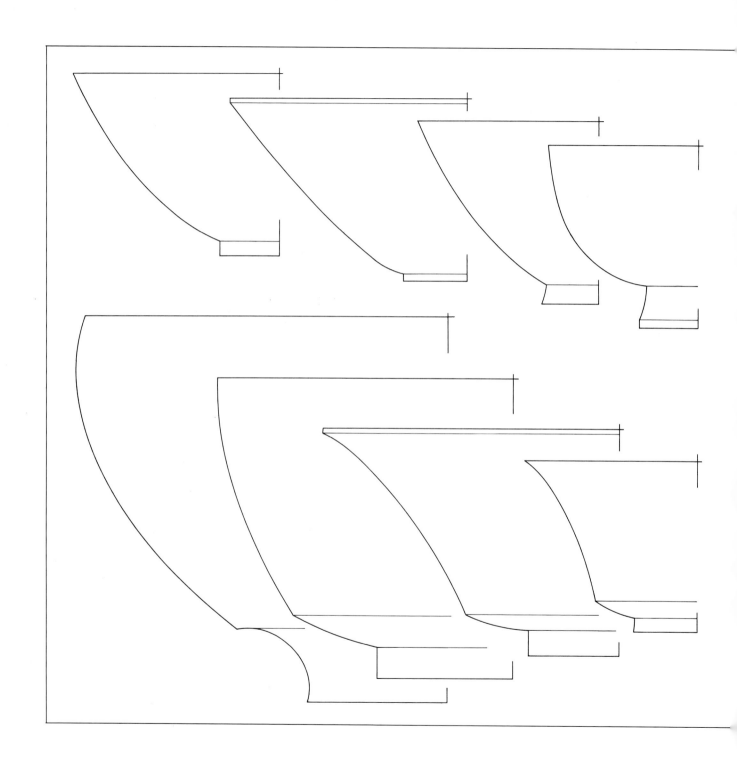

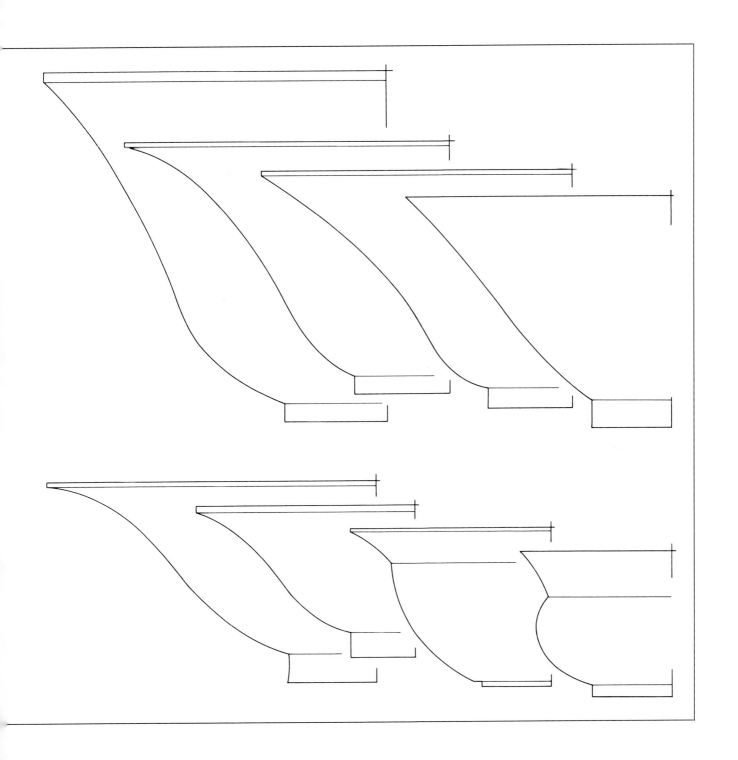

Green-Turning

IF you turn a bowl from unseasoned timber, it will warp. While generations of turners have tried to overcome this normally irritating trait, it can be used to advantage—given the proper material and approach. Turning bowls from green wood is nothing new. Bowl-roughing techniques have been around for at least 150 years, and probably much longer. But these days, "green-turning" has come to refer to the practice of turning and finishing bowls in unseasoned timber, with the intention of letting them warp.

I had been roughing bowls out of green timber for nearly five years before the notion of finishing one entered my tiny brain. A student asked me if there would be problems in finishing a bowl made from unseasoned timber. I said it would warp, and the retort was, "So what?". So I gave it a go, and that was how, in the late 1970s, I began to experiment with finishing green-turned bowls. In no time at all I was creating oval forms, or long, flowing, curved rims that looked anything but turned.

Later, I discovered that turners had been doing the same in other parts of the world. Suddenly green-turning was in vogue, and all manner of would-be turned *art* flooded the craft galleries. Worse, an eager public devoured it. Too many of these early green-turners were content, it seems, to let their bowls warp any old way in the hope that they would prove quirky enough to sell. Still others seemed to feel it their role to release the "spirit of the tree." Nearly a decade later, I am still disappointed by how few turners have

The warped holly bowls above, about 10-in. (255mm) diameter, were turned and finished from freshly felled timber. By paying careful attention to the choice of wood and to the grain alignment, the warp of green-turned bowls can be used with dramatic effect. At left, holly, 9½-in. (220mm) diameter, with a 1/16-in. (2mm) wall thickness.

In this 10-in.- (250mm) dia. elm bowl, made by Michael Peterson of Seattle, Washington, the tighter grain to the right of the rim distorted the form to create an undulating, oval opening.

made use of the real potential of green-turned wood. For the best results, you need the right even-grained material, cut the right way, and aligned precisely on the lathe to make the most of what will happen when the wood dries out. Even then, the hardest part is to come. After the bowl has twisted you must cast a critical eye over the result, and destroy the inferior pieces. A reputation for quality is built upon rigorous culling—rather like animal husbandry.

Your first task in turning wood—green wood, in particular—is to understand the material. You must be able to predict what it will do as it dries out. Not all woods are suitable. You need wood that will warp or twist without splitting, so avoid the well-known stable timbers such as teak, mahogany or iroko, as well as those that split easily, like olive. Instead, look for holly, or any of the oaks or fruitwoods.

To ascertain how a wood is likely to distort during seasoning, slice a thin board of green timber, about 8 in. (200mm) square and ⅛ in. (3mm) thick. (Avoid quartersawn stock, which will shrink evenly across its grain rather than twist.) Leave the test board in the sun for a few hours, or cook it in a microwave oven for a minute or two. If it hardly moves, try another species. If it twists dramatically, it could be just what you're looking for. Then test how easily it might bend, break or split. If it's strong, use it.

The way a bowl warps is dictated by its grain and shape and how the two relate. Closed forms, like the one at left, and those with nearly vertical walls, should become oval if the wood is even-grained, devoid of knots and other defects, and aligned with its pith in the center of either the base or rim. Outflowing forms, like the casuarina bowls below, will undulate. These two bowls were turned within a few hours of the tree being felled, to obtain the maximum amount of shrinkage in drying.

These 7½-in.- (190mm) dia. casuarina bowls, which were turned and finished within one day of felling the 8-in.- (200mm) dia. tree, display extreme warping.

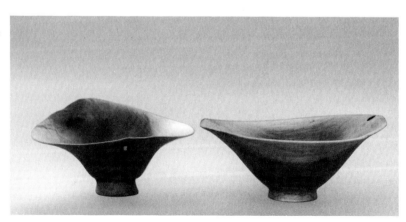

The bowls pictured in the top photo at right show how similar but larger blanks, cut lower down from the same tree, will distort in different forms. In both, the pith of the tree runs across the center of the rim. In the bowl on the right, the pith has pulled up, creating sides that slope away and an attractive boat shape. In the enclosed bowl on the left, the pith also peaks up, but produces a less satisfactory rim as it mars the flow of line. Had this blank been cut without the pith, like the liquid-amber bowl below, the rim warp would have been much more subtle.

I made the three 10-in.- (255mm) dia. holly bowls shown on the top of p. 119 about ten years ago. Their uneven growth rings created little bumps on the rim, but the basic line of the profile remains largely undistorted.

The blanks for the 7-in.- (175mm) dia. banksia bowls at right were aligned with the pith slightly off-center so that the warping would be biased to one side. The danger with this technique is that shrinkage can leave the bowl so far off balance that it is fit only for the woodpile. On the left bowl, the rim has pulled down just enough to create an interesting line, but not enough to topple the bowl. The bowl on the right warped to the point of instability, so I sanded the base parallel to the rim. This makes the form look a bit wind-blown, like a tree regularly buffeted by high winds.

The wood will bump up if the pith lies on the rim, as in the 10-in.- (255mm) dia. casuarina bowls at top. Above, uneven distortion occurs if the pith is aligned off-center.

This 14¾-in.- (375mm) dia. liquid-amber bowl was turned from wood felled three weeks before. The surface is unsanded, straight from the ½-in. (13mm) deep-fluted gouge.

Timber always distorts more in areas of stress—around crotches or knots. If you include one knot or an area of tighter grain, such as the pith, in an otherwise even-grained bowl, you will get more distortion in that area. In both of the bowls below the pith is located halfway down the bowl wall. This causes pointed bulges in some parts of the wall and flat spots in others. These bowls are examples of the worst of green-wood turnery, and I made them expressly to illustrate the point that all that twists is not art.

The 6-in.- (150mm) dia. mushroom bowl on the facing page, on the other hand, is an example of stressed timber used to advantage. The blank for this bowl came from a knotty crotch of green plum. The grain runs almost vertically up the stem and flows through the edge of a knot into the bowl. The pith runs across the bowl just below the rim to create the upward sweep at both ends. The knot at the base of the bowl was included to tilt the bowl slightly to one side. The main problem in such a form is the near certainty that the foot will split unless the grain runs its length. So a form like this has to come from a branch that projects at a right angle from the trunk of the tree.

The drier your wood, the less distortion you will get. Many of what I consider my most successful bowls are roughed soon after the tree is felled and finished two or three weeks later, when much

These bowls display the grotesque distortion that typically results when little attention is given to grain alignment.

An unusual branch at a right angle to the trunk of a tree created the opportunity to produce this 6-in.- (150mm) dia. fungal form.

of the surface moisture has evaporated. The bowls on the top of the facing page are fine examples of the subtle distortion that can occur in a partially dried blank.

When conducting workshops or demonstrations, I have found that there is a widely held belief that turning green wood is somehow different and much more difficult than working seasoned material. The main difference is that wet wood works a darn sight more easily. There's no mystery to the turning, and only a little in the alignment of the grain. In essence, there are only two real problems: finishing and, if the wood is thin, coping with its fragility.

Wet timber can be difficult to sand using conventional abrasives, since these quickly become clogged and soggy. You can allow the abrasive to dry and knock out the dust, but this is tedious. Also, the metal in some abrasives will discolor many light-colored woods. Certain pale timbers, such as holly, are more susceptible to this than others.

Wet-or-dry abrasives are one solution, but remember that electricity and water don't mix, and most lathe manufacturers don't recommend the use of water near their machines. I prefer to dry the wood surface enough to sand, but not enough to distort the bowl. A couple of minutes in a microwave oven might do the job, but this is likely to distort the form. A better bet is to apply external heat that will evaporate the surface moisture without affecting the inside. I use a small propane torch, but a good electric hair dryer would be less dangerous.

The need to support a bowl wall becomes more acute as it gets thinner. A thin wall turned in wet timber is very fragile and flexible, and it is easily destroyed by the slightest pressure from the tool. There are two ways to cope with this, but before you try either one, finish-sand the outside. This gives you an exact surface to which the inside can relate, and will leave you with less sanding at the very end, when the bowl is most fragile.

The best approach is to use one hand for support behind the bowl wall to absorb any pressure from the tool, as shown at the bottom of the facing page. I generally cut the entire wall down to around ¼ in. (6mm), and then take two cuts as quickly and as fluently as possible to arrive at the final wall thickness. You don't have much time to mess around with very thin walls—the wood starts to move the moment it gets thin. You get only one shot at any wall less than ⅛ in. (3mm) thick. The best way to develop the required speed is to rough out a lot of green bowls, using a small gouge and trying to get the best possible cut with each pass.

These 15-in.- (385mm) dia. banksia bowls were roughed from a fresh-cut log, then finish-turned and fumed with ammonia three weeks later.

Very thin bowls require support during turning. The fingers can be used to counteract tool pressure, and the thumb provides a fulcrum.

If you don't have the speed, you will need to adopt the more time-consuming method of developing the wall in steps. With this method, you thin down ¾-in.- (20mm) long sections of wall at a time, beginning at the rim. The rest of the bowl, which is yet unturned, prevents distortion of the thinner section. It is much more difficult to turn a good flowing line using this technique, because you never get to watch the whole sweep of the curve develop. As a result, the form is likely to lack the spontaneity that can result from a single flowing cut.

With pale timbers, it pays to have a strong light behind the wall so you can observe the progress of your cut. Water transmits a lot of light, so the wall will often appear thinner than it actually is, which is worth bearing in mind if you want to ham it up before an audience. Unfortunately, darker timbers do not transmit light, so to judge their thickness you'll have to rely on your sense of touch or on calipers, in combination with the cutting sounds. You can gauge thickness much more rapidly with sensitive fingers, but these take time to develop. As usual, there's no substitute for experience. Cultivate early the habit of measuring by hand and eye, before using instruments to check yourself. Soon you should be able to rely more on your senses, checking only occasionally to ensure that you are on the right track.

Although it will almost certainly warp, once a green-turned bowl has been successfully finished, it is unlikely to split. But bear in mind the seasoning guidelines discussed in Chapter 3 for roughed-out bowls. You can make the wall as thick as you like, but bowl walls in excess of 2 in. (50mm) thick could take a couple of years to dry out completely. If it dries out slowly, it might not even warp that much, although the surface can collapse, producing a really interesting texture, as shown on the top of the facing page. These smooth, jarrah-burl bowls are developing an undulating surface not unlike that of a walnut shell or an orange peel. On a more open-grained wood, the softer areas will collapse, leaving little ridges of harder grain. In the bowl at the bottom of the facing page, for example, the softer areas have collapsed, leaving flecks of harder grain slightly proud of the surface—a wonderful surface to feel and hold.

Perhaps the best thing of all about turning green wood is that you can produce a top-quality, finished piece in less time than you can in almost any other branch of woodworking.

A bright light is the best way to judge wall thickness in pale woods.

The rims of these jarrah-burl bowls are beginning to crumple as the wood dries out.

This round-bottomed bowl was rough-turned and left for four weeks before being finished. The surface is drying to the texture of old, polished leather. Casuarina river oak, 16-in. (405mm) diameter.

Surface Decoration

THIS chapter is about bowl surfaces and the details or textures that may be applied to them to highlight proportion or to enhance their tactile qualities. At the end of the chapter I discuss some common natural defects to be found in wood, and suggest how they may (or may not) be incorporated into your work.

Most woodturners like to get a head start on the design process by working with highly figured, colorful timber. But don't rely on extravagant color or grain to carry your work. These characteristics will not last unless the wood is protected from light, air and especially use, any of which will cause wood to mellow, fade or darken. A few decades will render all but the strongest grain patterns barely discernable. Only quilted or fiddleback patterns will shine through the aging process. Even the strong grain patterns in the grass-tree bowl on the facing page, far right, will eventually be enveloped by the darkening wood. Grain ought to be used sparingly as a design element, anyway—too strong a pattern can easily overwhelm a small bowl.

So many woods are a treat to work, but lack dramatic grain. (Nearly all the commercial hardwoods fall into this category.) Rosewood mahogany, for example, works well and holds detailed beading and crisp edges, but is basically dull. Like so many timbers, it is pale when freshly turned, and soon mellows with exposure to light. It would be a pity to avoid such a wonderful wood, which can provide the perfect medium for expressing form.

Dale Nish's wormy-ash bowl is an excellent
example of what can be achieved if the curve is
just right. The dramatic defects and sandblasted
surface are striking, but secondary to the form.

The grain pattern overwhelms this grass-tree
bowl and is better suited to a much larger form.

But without a grain pattern to break the surface, even the most elegant form may be too stark. A well-placed line or bit of texture may be just what's needed for visual interest. Limited use of decoration can do wonders for a bowl. But try to resist the temptation to smother a bowl with all manner of decorative tricks—restrained application is the key to success.

Turned decoration

Beads, grooves and coves can be used to break up a form horizontally or to emphasize a rim or foot. In the beautiful little bowl at left, the smallest bead is at the foot, and the beads enlarge gradually as the diameter increases, each being the right size for its position in the curve. Note how the line of the curve is maintained along the fullness of each bead.

Individual beads or pairs of beads can be inset, like those on the 19th-century whey bowl below, or can be turned on the surface, like the ones on p. 97. The inset beads that encircle the rim of the bowl at the top of the facing page also break the surface nicely and help define the rim. Likewise, inset beads can be employed to create a formal border within an eccentric, and rougher, profile, as on the jarrah-burl bowl in the photo at the center of p. 79. If raised above the surface, beads should not interfere with the flow of the line beneath. They should look like they were applied after the profile was cut. This is difficult to achieve, but all is not lost if you make a mess of them—you can always remove a bead and try a groove instead.

Grooves are quicker and easier to make than beads and have much the same impact, a benefit worth noting if you are in business. I use grooves to highlight a rim, or to relieve a hard angle or the sparseness of a plain foot. The groove on the waney-edged elm-burl bowl at the bottom of the facing page not only relieves the harshness of the foot, it served a practical function while the bowl was turned, by locating the rim of the 1½-in. spigot chuck.

This bowl was made by Del Stubbs of Chico, California, during a demonstration at Canberra in 1986. Tasmanian myrtle, 6-in.- (150mm) diameter.

Whoever made this old bowl shows a fine sense of proportion in the application of inset beads. From a private collection.

Inset beads encircle the rim and decorate the bland surface of this rosewood mahogany bowl.

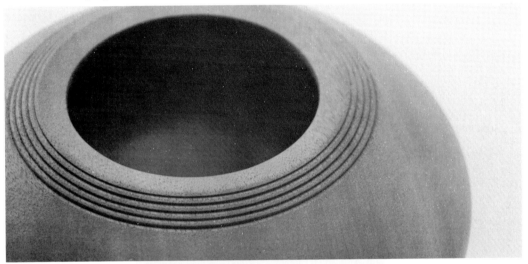

The grooved foot on this 7-in.- (180mm) dia. elm-burl bowl was used to locate the rim of the spigot chuck. The bowl was made decorative rather than functional by the presence of the low hole.

Grooves are most effective on convex surfaces. The deep groove on the jarrah-burl bowl at left below marks the edge of the rim, which curves out of the groove and rolls over the top towards the interior. Likewise, grooves can be used to highlight the warp of a rim, as shown in the bowl below.

On the liquid-amber bowl at bottom, I cut a single spiral up from the base. This rough-sided groove was incised into the finished surface to provide a contrast with the smooth bowl wall. I used a shallow gouge, ground to a fingernail edge to make this cut. The gouge was held at a right angle to the wood's surface, with the lathe running slowly—around 100 rpm. It's very difficult to move the tool quickly and evenly around the curve to turn a good spiral, but it is worth the effort when you get it right. Practice on wood you can afford to waste, perhaps during the early stages of roughing. Cut the

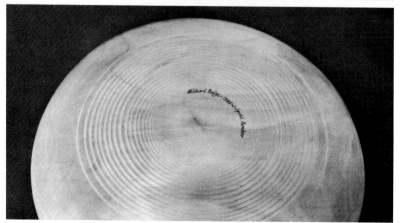

The outer edge of the rim on the jarrah-burl bowl above is defined by a deep groove. The distorted rim of the 15-in.- (380mm) dia. green-turned banksia bowl, top right, is emphasized by the groove around it. One continuous spiral, cut into the finished surface, decorates the base of the 16-in. (405mm) liquid-amber bowl, right.

groove into a smoothed, curved surface, moving the tool rapidly from the smaller to larger diameter.

Grooves also can be grouped up and down on the wall of a bowl, as shown below, to create rough bands of texture. On this bowl I left smooth bands between short, spiral cuts. The cut grooves were brushed lightly to soften the torn, long grain.

In many of the profile drawings in Chapter 4, you will have noticed the use of beads or coves at a point of transition, perhaps where the bowl wall meets the foot, or where the rim flares out from the wall. These beads are used to soften otherwise harsh angles and as a link between two adjacent surfaces. In the bowl shown in the photo at the bottom of the page, for example, Ray Key of Evesham, England, used little grooved steps to link the three surfaces.

The casuarina bowl at left was finished three weeks after the tree was felled, and rough-turned. The grooves were meant to distort slightly, but the upper wall could have curved in more to form a narrower rim. At bottom left, shadow highlights the form and the grooves that join the adjacent surfaces on Ray Key's 15-in.- (380mm) dia. English-ash bowl.

Texture Texture can work wonders in enhancing an object's tactile quality. Consider the clean-cut surface left by a gouge. It will have a unique character, unobtainable with abrasives. It is my sad experience, however, that a good finish straight from the tool is virtually unmarketable today. It's not rough enough for the hair-shirt brigade, nor smooth enough for the jet set (and I suppose not shiny enough for the masses between). As a result, I finish few bowls this way. It's a pity, though, because the subtle marks of skillful tool handling can greatly enhance an object's appeal.

In the photo below is a liquid-amber bowl that I turned as smoothly as possible and left unsanded. For the final outside cut, I made one fluid movement with a deep-fluted gouge. The inside was cut in two stages, using both gouge and scraper. The form oozes spontaneity, while the tool finish is beautifully soft to the touch, although not mirror-smooth. I regularly use this bowl for bread-making, and the patina is developing nicely—in a few years it should be truly wonderful.

I turned a series of facets on the profile of the liquid-amber bowl shown in the photo at left below, and stained the inside dark. A tool-finished profile can also provide a nice contrast with a sanded and polished interior. The reverse arrangement—a rough interior and smooth outside—is usually unsuccessful, however, because of the general perception that a rough interior isn't practical or desirable.

Wire brushing adds texture to the surface of this elm bowl.

The facets on the liquid-amber profile above are unsanded and were singed with a propane torch to accentuate the ridges. The bowl at right, also unsanded, was finished in one fluid movement with a deep-fluted gouge. Then the bowl was decorated with a spiral groove.

With regular use and care, all these bowls eventually will develop the wonderful patina common to so many old bowls. Some of the finest such examples are in the Pinto Collection of Treen, two of which are shown below. The tool marks show through in places, but have been mostly worn away by steady use. This collection of over 7,000 small wooden objects is something that all woodworkers should try to see.

The handle on the 6-in. (150mm) bowl above is all that remains of a wide, turned rim. The wonderful spiral inside the 4½-in. (115mm) bowl at left is all the more remarkable in that it was probably created in the speed of production, when getting a hollow was all that mattered. Two bowls from the Pinto Collection of Treen in the City Museum and Art Gallery, Birmingham, England.

Texture and contrast also can be created by wearing away the softer grain more rapidly than harder areas, or by carving into a finished surface. While the former can be done quickly using wire or nylon brushes, or by sandblasting, carving is an entirely different matter. For a really good job, you need the skills of another wood-working craft, although you might get by with some simple, well-placed techniques, such as the shallow, vertical gouge marks on the bowl at top on the facing page. As with beads and grain patterns, the restrained application of texture has the greatest impact.

Sandblasting is the best way to remove soft areas of grain to produce a weathered effect. Don't expect the process to eliminate signs of poor workmanship—it is more likely to highlight them. Surfaces must be well finished, because any scratch will be worn down evenly along with the surface it scars. The best results usually come from timber with a pronounced difference between the hard latewood and the soft earlywood of the growth rings.

In the photo at left on p. 129, you can see how a powerful sand-blasting jet has etched out the soft earlywood (and bugs) of Dale Nish's wormy-ash bowl. Unfortunately, very few amateurs can afford tools that are capable of such ruthless scouring. You might find a friendly sandblaster in the metalworking department of a nearby college, or perhaps among local builders or automotive tradesmen.

I have discovered other, less expensive ways of creating similar surfaces using wire or nylon brushes. A hand-held wire brush applied to the revolving wood, for example, will excavate the softer grain but leave striations. To inset the band of texture in the smooth bowl surface at center on the facing page, I cut two grooves to mark the edges first, and then reduced the surface between them before holding a heavy wire brush to the revolving wood.

The surface of the elm bowl at top left on p. 134 was created by applying a drill-mounted wire brush against the revolving bowl. As with sandblasting, it is important to start with a good surface. A similar but softer nylon brush will do a good job. This leaves a much cleaner surface than does a wire brush, with virtually no scratch marks. The manufacturers claim these will outlast the wire brushes and do the same job, but I find they don't scour out the softer grain quite as ruthlessly.

On the elm bowl at the bottom of the facing page, the smooth rim stands out against the rest of the wire-brushed profile. To keep a crisp line between the rough and smooth sections, finish the wall to the bottom of the rim band, which should be left over-thick. Apply the brush to the lower surface, and then cut and sand the rim, taking care to leave a crisp edge where it meets the brushed wall.

TURNED-
BOWL
DESIGN
136

Garth May of Dublin, Ireland, uses simple carving to enhance his bowl rims and sides. Here, the carved band is set off by a pair of turned coves.

The wire-brushed striations encircle the 13¼-in.- (335mm) dia. Sally-wattle bowl at left. The grain of the elm bowl at bottom left, like that of ash or locust, is ideally suited to brushing.

Very heavy sanding using 60-grit abrasive will produce a subtle undulating surface on open-grained timber. Using this method, you can easily imitate the effect of several decades of active use, but scratch marks left by the coarser grits are difficult to remove because of the undulating surface they produce. This can be overcome by sanding at a low speed.

Rough sawcuts can also provide some interesting surfaces. I left the rim of the jarrah-burl bowl at center on the facing page wide to display the chainsawn ridges that were on the original blank. The rough rim contrasts nicely with the smoothly turned interior and exterior profiles, although the lump on the far edge leaves the form a trifle unbalanced. I buffed the surface using the drill-mounted nylon wheel, and hand-sanded the edges for safety. On the jarrah bowl at the bottom of the facing page, the chainsaw marks disrupt the otherwise flat rim just enough to be interesting. The bandsawn striations on the seven- and nine-sided bowls on p. 106 demonstrate another decorative application of saw marks.

Color

As I stated in the Introduction, this book is concerned with bowls that are manifestly made of wood. A number of contemporary turners are coating their bowls with layers of epoxy resin or paint to create wonderful objects, but these techniques obliterate the wood. However, it is possible to color your bowl using stains or dyes, by fuming with ammonia or by charring the surface in such a way that the grain still shows through.

Stains and dyes

The use of pigments is another specialized field with which I flirted briefly around eight years ago. I like the idea of tinting pale timbers, such as the liquid-amber bowl at bottom left on p. 134, so that the grain and natural color of the wood intrudes less on our perception of the form. But I want my bowls to be used, preferably for food, and, apart from food dyes, I know of no stain that is guaranteed safe for human consumption. I used these dyes for a while, with only limited success. (Standard wood stains are fine if you are certain that no one will ever use the bowl for food.) Safety aside, because the side and end grain absorb moisture at different rates, I found it nearly impossible to get an even stain using food dyes. The thicker and darker the stain, the better the coverage, but the more it obscured the grain—I couldn't win.

Of course, solid pigments can be applied—in limited doses—to highlight a form or create an interesting effect. Working in the far north of Scotland, Liz and Michael O'Donnell spray cellulose-based

The surface of this open-grained, Chinese-elm bowl undulates dramatically after heavy sanding.

A wire brush is too abrasive for the chainsawn surface of the rim at right. A nylon brush—hand-held or mounted in an electric drill—removes the muck without obliterating the distinct saw marks. Looking like some well-worn mountain range, the chainsawn rim below provides another solution to coping with a stark profile.

melamine mixed with oil paint on their decorative bowls, shown on pp. 156 and 169. Likewise, Leslie John Wright of Perth, Western Australia, uses color to transform his bowls, shown on p. 164, into more decorative objects. In both cases, the results are dramatic, but do not overwhelm the skillful turnery and design.

Inlay is yet another way to introduce color. Two of the simplest methods involve letting a strip of colored wood into a groove, or gluing colored plugs (or plugs of different kinds of woods) into round holes, such as those shown at the top of the facing page. In the bowl at the bottom of the facing page, Ray Cornu of Shannon, Ireland, laminated walnut and ash in three layers to create graphic patterns.

Chemical coloring   Fuming with ammonia will darken any timber that has a high tannin content, such as oak or eucalyptus. You will quickly discover if a wood contains much tannin—it stains your hands black, particularly if the wood is freshly cut. The simplest way to fume a bowl is to seal it inside a tent made from a plastic bag, along with an open container holding about two cups of ammonia. (Household ammonia will work, but the more expensive ammonia you can buy at a pharmacy is better and stronger.) The fuming period will vary considerably, depending on the timber and how dark you want it. I figure about two weeks maximum, but it's a good idea to check the color daily. The gases must be able to circulate freely around the wood, so you should construct a simple frame to keep the plastic off the wood. You can place a cardboard box in the bag or erect a tripod of small sticks, like an Indian tepee. In either case, secure the opening of the bag so that the fumes cannot escape. And don't forget to hold your breath when you open the bag—the fumes are not pleasant.

If you rest the bowl on its base, the bottom will not change color because the gases cannot reach the wood's surface; if you rest the bowl on its rim, you can fume the outside without affecting the interior. If you want the bowl fumed all over, balance it on the edge of the rim and rotate it daily to prevent any light spots. The fumes will darken all the exposed surfaces evenly, although they penetrate farther into the more porous end grain than into the long grain. This means that if you fume a roughed-out bowl you'll get color variations when you turn it true. These variations are often very subtle and may be attractive, but they won't last. Light and air soon eliminate all but the most extreme discrepancies. As an added bonus, I find that the sanded surface of many woods feels much smoother, almost silky, after fuming.

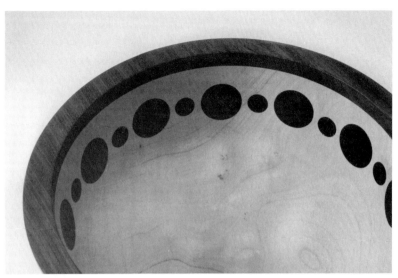

Inlaid plugs, above, and laminates, at left, of different woods can be used to create interesting effects in turned bowls.

Tannin also reacts with iron, creating a dark blue-to-purple stain. A nail hammered into an oak or yew tree will cause localized discoloration, while a finished bowl of the same wood, left to soak in water containing iron, will turn dark blue in a few days. The result can resemble bog-oak, or other timbers that have been blackened by centuries-long immersion in swamp water. The metal dust from around your grinder, if sprinkled on a damp wood surface, can create blue speckling.

Fire The huon-pine log on the facing page was already charred when I bought it, so I decided to burn the profile to match the rim and to contrast with the golden interior. I used an oxyacetylene torch, which enabled me to burn right into the splits, but I have used a small propane torch with equal effect. In case the torch wandered, I saved the final hollowing cuts until after the charring process.

When you burn wood there is a fair amount of soot and charcoal to remove, and I keep an old scrub brush specifically for the job. Once all the loose rubbish is off, I use an 8-in. (200mm) cloth buffing wheel to polish the surface. If the bowl is on the lathe I mount the buffing wheel in an electric drill and apply it to the rotating bowl. If the bowl is off the lathe, as it must be to clean the base, I mount the buffing wheel on the lathe and apply the bowl's surface to it.

I highlighted the facets on the bowl profile on p. 134, bottom left, by using a propane torch to char the ridges slightly. This is a handy way to accent the angles on grooved rims or beads, but be careful not to overdo it. You want a lightly charred brown, not a burnt black.

Pyrography is a method of burning wood using a red-hot steel point. The use of pyrography to decorate turned objects has a long tradition in many parts of the world, particularly in Scandinavia and central and eastern Europe, where turned bowls and platters have been adorned with village scenes and geometric patterns.

You no longer have to heat up the fireplace poker, although Guy Martin's bowl at the bottom of p. 160 uses precisely this technique. In recent years, many electric pyrographic machines have appeared on the market. These consist of a small transformer with a temperature control dial, or rheostat, attached by cable to a cumbersome pen, which holds the point. Many of these machines are used solely for signing completed work, although they were designed for burning designs into wood.

The pyrographic pens work well on close- and even-grained light-colored woods, against which the black line will stand out. All the machines I have used, however, leave a lot to be desired on

Great care is needed when charring, to preserve the crisp edges between the rim and walls.

hard or uneven surfaces. The problem seems to lie in the wire point. If it is fine enough for small writing it will bend. If it is thick enough to retain its shape, it will not get red hot (it will still char the wood, but slowly). The more elaborate systems offer an assortment of points and brands that lend themselves well to decorating a bowl rim or foot. In the absence of one of these products, you can always resort to less sophisticated methods—such as heating the end of a pipe to brand circles around a rim.

There are all kinds of variations you might dream up to enhance your bowls, a few of which are shown in the Gallery. Just remember to exercise a little restraint in their application.

Using defects When I began to turn wood in the early 1970s, the slightest defect in a bowl rendered it a second, fit only to be sold cheaply and anonymously or, more often, for direct consignment to the firewood pile. I recall two bowls in particular from those days. One was a large teak bowl with a couple of tiny worm holes near the rim, which today would worry few people. The other was a cream-colored maple bowl that was utterly bland, except for a wisp of black stain across its center—in those days a major blemish. Times have changed. The black stain, in particular, would now be regarded as a bonus, and would likely inflate the price of the bowl.

My attitude towards splits and other defects has always remained, rather boringly I'm afraid, much the same. I prefer clean material without any defects, although every now and then I come across a log with some extraordinary feature that even I can't pass by. I have incorporated some of these into bowls, initially to satisfy my own curiosity and subsequently to meet market demands. Increasingly, this practice has been forced upon me by the need to make the best of expensive material. If you are going to include what might reasonably be regarded as a defect, you must finish it as well as the rest of the bowl. It should be perfectly clear that you intended the defect to be included, and that it was detailed accordingly. (Vic Wood's bowl on p. 161, top, is a good example of this.)

Splits These can be filled and made to blend in with the surrounding wood. Or you can draw attention to them by filling them with a brightly colored material or by carving them. Of course, you can also leave them as they are, a feature in their own right. The old, dry jarrah burl at left is unlikely to split further. Before sanding, the splits were brushed vigorously to soften the corners and to remove splinters and unwanted livestock.

Air passing through the unfilled splits of this 12-in.- (305mm) dia. jarrah bowl would make this a fine fruit container.

Narrow splits along the grain can be disguised in dark woods using a cyanoacrylate "super" glue or an epoxy resin. The former will bond in about 15 seconds, or less if used with an accelerator. It's very expensive, but its speed and convenience make the cost worthwhile in production. If the split is ultra-thin, you can use a low-viscosity epoxy to penetrate the crack. Splits ⅟₃₂ in. (1mm) wide require a more viscous, gap-filling resin (add an accelerator if you don't fancy waiting five minutes for the epoxy to set). You can match the filling to the wood by adding some sawdust or small shavings to the resin as it sets. The hardened filling may be turned, sanded and polished along with the rest of the surface. This technique rarely works with pale timbers because the resin (even the clear variety) looks dark and will darken any sawdust that's added to it.

If the crack is large enough, you can lay a shaving the length of the split before pouring in the resin. Make sure the glue is allowed to penetrate the split before spraying on the accelerator. Done properly, this resembles a natural fibrous intrusion, which is exactly what it is, even if it did not occur naturally.

There is little point in trying to fill a split that runs across the growth rings—it will be impossible to disguise. What's more, the filler will remain inert while the wood shrinks, expands and darkens with age. An intrusion across the grain will always stand out, while a similar filling along the grain will feel like just a quirk in the wood. You would be better off using a mechanical fastening to hold such a split together, though perhaps not so basic a device as that used on the old dairy bowl below. A leather thong, or a silver or stainless-steel wire could substitute nicely for the heavy iron staple.

A heavy iron staple provides a basic remedy against further splitting. This approach was once common—the protruding points are clenched on the inner wall to secure the staple.

Detailing generally involves carving, beveling, sanding or buffing a feature, rather than leaving it rough. I find short splits—either along or across the grain—acceptable for detailing if located high up on the bowl wall. If placed too low in the bowl, such details arouse all sorts of subliminal notions about practicality and function. The split in the bowl in the photo below is acceptable only because the bowl profile is exceptional. The split lies rather low

The split so near the bottom of this large salad bowl is unfortunate, but the form is strong enough to overcome such a piffling defect.

in the wall and is obtrusive, so I usually try to hide that side from view. Even if filled with epoxy, the split might detract from the whole.

The split in the bowl at the top of the facing page is too long and dominates the form. By detailing the split, it appears that the maker tried to come to terms with his misfortune. Had there been more splits to detail, the form might have been quite interesting.

When nearly completed, thin-walled bowls split from the rim, I used to throw them on the fire. That was before I started carving them into petal-like rims, like the ones at the bottom of the facing page. I soon realized that heart shakes are ideal for such detailing and I began looking for suitable splits, especially in green timber. The bowl at far right on the facing page is almost mundane beside the holly bowl at bottom left; there I was able to distort the outward flow of the rim slightly upwards where it curves into the split.

This technique works best on fine, outflowing, footed forms, turned from green timber, but such petal-like detailing doesn't work on thicker forms. Besides the fact that the wood is difficult to distort, the whole notion is clumsy—petals are associated with delicacy, not mass. Any crack might split further, so you should finish the detailing well, which will reassure a prospective customer that you have considered the defect, and that it has stabilized.

Even sanded smooth and rounded, this split still looks like a defect. Four or five smaller splits in the same bowl might have looked better.

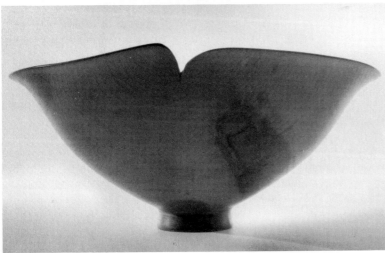

The wings of the split on the outflowing rim of the 7-in. (180mm) holly bowl, left, were effectively distorted, while the smaller stinkwood bowl, above, failed to respond to a similar treatment.

Bark intrusions I only rarely include bark within a bowl wall because, unless the wood is very stable, the bark and wood will shrink at different rates. Sooner or later the two will part company, regardless of glues or resins. The huon-pine bowl below comes from a tree fork, at a point where the bark intruded well into the wood. Huon pine is a stable timber, so I decided to leave the bark and to stabilize it using a cyanoacrylate gap filler. The bark was turned

You should risk retaining bark like this only when you are sure that movement in the surrounding wood will be minimal.

along with the rest of the wall and then liberally coated with the resin, which was allowed to soak in before the accelerator was applied to harden it. I like the shape of this intrusion and the way it sits between the two naturally resinous patches of end grain.

Spalted woods When I was still wet behind the ears, I asked a local production turner about how to cut a piece of slightly spalted ash. "We call that incipient rot in the trade," he said, "and would throw it out for firewood if it gave any heat. We usually just throw it out." As it happens, I didn't follow his advice. I soon found that spalted wood sells well, although it almost always looks flat, dull and somewhat dead, which is exactly what it is. Although, this much can be said for it: Once it's oiled and polished, spalted timber is unlikely to deteriorate.

I prefer to use wood in which I can place more faith, and which glows with the luster of top-grade material. But since spalted timber is very popular and I have a living to earn, I will use it if the piece isn't too soft. If I can make a groove in the wood easily with my fingernail, then it is rejected. Apart from any objection I might have to its appearance, such material is difficult to hold on the lathe and can be dangerous to turn. It's also hard to cut cleanly, which usually means that heavy sanding is required for a reasonable finish.

The small area of rotted wood near the rim of the bowl below was stabilized using a thin, cyanoacrylate glue. The foot of the bowl at bottom also has a patch of soft, spalted wood that I was tempted to retain for decoration. Rather than risk the softer material wearing away before the adjacent wood, however, I decided to turn away the whole foot. That done, I feel confident that the bowl can last a few centuries.

Thin, cyanoacrylate glue will soak into pithy grain like water in a sponge, and will stabilize almost any soft wood. But it is an expensive technique.

This spalted patch could have been stabilized with glue, but instead, the foot was turned away entirely, leaving solid material.

Holes In general, holes, like splits, need to be kept as high up on the bowl wall as possible, as in the mulga bowl below. There is something unsettling about one hole or split in the bottom of a vessel—it always looks odd and unintentional. A few more holes usually appear less haphazard, but may still create the impression, perhaps untrue, that the form can't function properly. Holes in the bottom of a fruit bowl will ensure a flow of air, which should help prevent the contents from rotting.

There are holes that just make it, and holes that don't—sometimes with only a fine line between the two. In the holly bowl at the top of the facing page, the hole is a bit too low, although the hole looks better than the knot ever did. A more desirable location for the hole would be nearer the rim. The single hole in the bottom of the elm-burl bowl on p. 131 is less objectionable because of the combination of the bowl's excellent form and wild grain pattern. The bowl at bottom right on the facing page also survives because the dramatic timber carries the defects. In both bowls at the bottom of the facing page, however, the holes are either unbalanced or too near the bottom; a few more of them might have had a totally different impact.

One of my favorite examples of a form riddled with holes is Dale Nish's well-eaten ash bowl at left on p. 129. It's worth noting that the bowl's success has at least as much to do with its spectacular form and dramatic grain pattern, as with the sandblasted worm holes.

Unless they appear in clusters, holes are not as unsettling if located well up on the bowl wall.

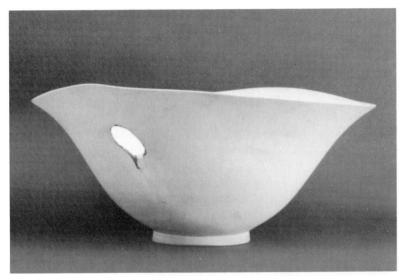

When the knot split, it was pushed out to create the hole. The bowl survives on the strength of its form, but it would look even better if the hole were ½ in. (13mm) higher.

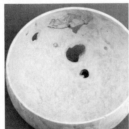

The location of the holes on one side and in the bottom of these bowls makes them visually unsettling and impractical.

Knots These vary enormously in size and behavior and, although their grain patterns are often dramatic, I generally try to avoid them—especially the larger ones. While some knots might remain inert and whole forever, most will either stay put and split or loosen and fall out. However, if I know the wood is fairly dry (below 20% moisture content), I will sometimes take a chance and include a whole knot, often with spectacular results.

I've found that in stable woods, most knots loosen only slightly, and they can be permanently fixed with a quick application of cyanoacrylate glue. With this treatment, the knot in the cherry bowl below has now survived seven years of hard labor as a serving dish. The knot in the casuarina bowl at bottom left on the preceding page split, but remained secure in the wood. I tried detailing it by sanding it smooth, which might have worked if the defect had been high up on the wall. As it is, the bowl is suitable only as a warning to fellow turners on the problems of knotty bottoms.

To every rule, there is an exception. The knot in the bottom of the sassafras bowl on the facing page adds interest to what would otherwise be a bland center. It also works well between the two heartwood intrusions on the rim.

This little knot survives despite rough treatment. To keep it tight, it was zapped with cyanoacrylate glue.

The knot works well in the bottom of this otherwise bland Tasmanian sassafras bowl. It is balanced by the swirling grain patterns on the other side of the bowl and by the dark splashes of heartwood.

Gallery

Grass tree; 13-in. (330mm) diameter.

English sycamore; 10 in. (255mm) x 6 in. (150mm); Anthony Bryant, Porthleven, England. Bryant chamfered the rim on this ultra-thin bowl, and then highlighted it with a black felt-tipped marker.

Sycamore; 10 in. (255mm) x 4 in. (100mm); Liz and Michael O'Donnell, Thurso, Scotland. The green-stained interior contrasts nicely with the creamy profile. Note how the groove accents the crisply turned rim.

English ash; 13-in. (330mm) diameter. This bowl is typical of my more utilitarian production. The undercut inner lip creates a shadow that accents the form.

Pohutukawa; 18 in. (455mm) long; Ken Sagar, Putaruru, New Zealand. Sagar likes to live dangerously. This triple bowl was mounted three times on different centers, and counter-balanced as required. Note that all edges are crisp.

Assorted offcuts; 16½ in. (420mm) x 4½ in. (115mm); Max Krimmel, Boulder, Colorado. Guitarmaker Krimmel uses his offcuts to advantage. The final form is turned from bowl-shaped blanks built from scraps. The inset bowl is predominantly pine, while the detail below shows another bowl of similar construction, combining maple, ebony and odd pieces of tropical exotica. Note that the rim is one color, framing the patchwork below.

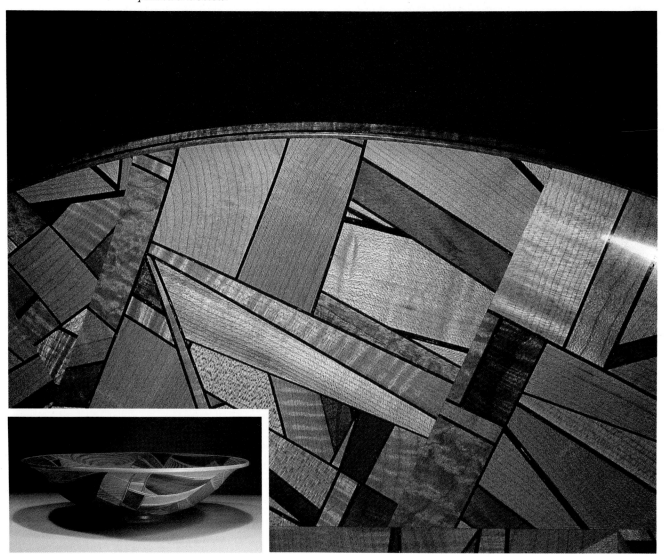

Rim detail; grass tree; 10-in. (255mm) diameter. This pitted section is the base of the trunk, which spawns the root system.

Right: English sycamore; 16-in. (405mm) outside-rim diameter. Below: English sycamore, burned and stained; 12-in. (305mm) diameter; Guy Martin, Ivybridge, England. Martin's fine-art training emerges in the rims of his bowls. The black slashes in the bowl below are burned in before the stain is applied. In the bowl at right, the smooth, turned surface of the internal rim is left, in part, to contrast with the carved sections below. Sycamore was selected for its bland color, its stability and its willingness to accept stain—a fine example of the material providing a lot of flexibility, but having little to say in the design.

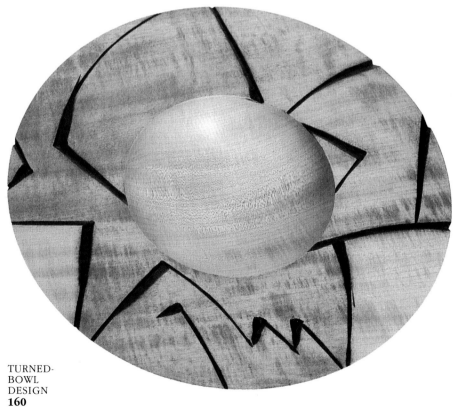

TURNED-
BOWL
DESIGN
160

Claret ash; 30-in. (760mm) square x 10 in. (255mm) high; Vic Wood, Melbourne, Australia. In this large bowl, Wood managed to keep two bark edges to contrast with the end-grain profiles. The crisp chamfer of the undulating bowl rim helps to define its borders. The heart splits have been detailed for added interest.

Quilted maple; 8-in. (200mm) diameter x 2½ in. (63mm) high. The rim was left wide to display the figure in the wood. Shallow beads around the inner lip break an otherwise stark form. The chamfer on the outer lip removes the vulnerable sharp edge, and makes the piece more sensual to hold. A squat foot lifts the form both visually and physically.

Top of facing page: Dorrel; 15-in. (380mm) diameter. This bowl was rough-turned between centers and transferred to a 3-in. (75mm) spigot chuck for hollowing. The shallow foot required by the chuck was removed on a belt sander and the round base was hand-finished.

Elm burl; 5-in. (125mm) diameter. The groove near the base of the foot serves a double purpose: It breaks the surface visually, and it provided a better grip for the jaws of the spigot chuck.

Huon pine; 9-in. (230mm) diameter; Stephen Hughes, Melbourne, Australia. The simplicity of the bowl makes the carved rim all the more striking.

Facing page: Grass tree; 8¾-in. (220mm) diameter; John Linek, Brisbane, Australia. A delightfully quirky bowl that makes full use of nature's idiosyncrasies. The fringe is the original root system of the plant, and not a separate addition.

Left: Marko's Slipway Series No. V; *casuarina, acrylic; 8½-in. (215mm) diameter. Below:* Cone Series No. III; *casuarina, buon pine, acrylic; 8-in. (200mm) diameter; Leslie John Wright, Perth, Australia.*

Sally wattle; 18-in. (455mm) diameter. The wire-brushed profile contrasts with the polished foot and interior.

Elm burl; 4-in. (100mm) diameter. A little round-bottomed nut bowl, meant to be held. A difference in grain density causes the list.

Cocobolo; 8 in. (200mm) x 3 in. (75mm); Alan Stirt, Enosburg, Vermont. A fine example of discreet carving, which contrasts with (but does not overpower) the smoother surfaces.

Banksia and casuarina; 6¾-in. (170mm) diameter. Green-turned and microwaved.

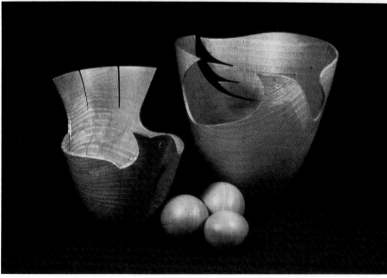

Above: Bowled Over; *sycamore with painted rims; 8-in. (200mm) to 10-in. (255mm) diameter.* Left: Bird Bowls; *beech; 4-in. (100mm) and 6-in. (150mm) diameters; Liz and Michael O'Donnell. The flat rim emphasizes the bird forms.*

Publisher, Books: Leslie Carola

Managing Editor: Deborah Cannarella

Associate Editor: Scott Landis

Design Director: Roger Barnes

Art Director: Ben Kann

Associate Art Director: Heather Brine Lambert

Layout Artists: Cathy Cassidy, Richard Erlanger

Copy/Production Editors: Victoria Monks, Nancy Stabile

Illustrations: Lee Hov

Director of Manufacturing: Kathleen Davis

Pre-Press Manager: Austin E. Starbird

Production Coordinators: Dave DeFeo, Ellen Olmsted

System Operators: Dinah George, Nancy-Lou Knapp

Production Assistants: Lisa Carlson, Mark Coleman, Deb Cooper

Pasteup: Marty Higham, Cynthia Lee Nyitray

Typeface: ITC Garamond Light, 10 pt.

Paper: Patina Matte, 70 lb., neutral pH

Printer and Binder: W.A. Krueger Co., New Berlin, Wisconsin